PART 5
ELASTIC–PLASTIC
FRACTURE MECHANICS

The Open University

T357
Structural integrity:
designing against failure

BLOCK 2
FRACTURE MECHANICS
PART 5

This publication forms part of an Open University course T357 *Structural integrity: designing against failure*. Details of this and other Open University courses can be obtained from the Student Registration and Enquiry Service, The Open University, PO Box 197, Milton Keynes MK7 6BJ, United Kingdom: tel. +44 (0)845 300 60 90, email general-enquiries@open.ac.uk

Alternatively, you may visit the Open University website at http://www.open.ac.uk where you can learn more about the wide range of courses and packs offered at all levels by The Open University.

To purchase a selection of Open University course materials visit http://www.ouw.co.uk, or contact Open University Worldwide, Michael Young Building, Walton Hall, Milton Keynes MK7 6AA, United Kingdom for a brochure. tel. +44 (0)1908 858793; fax +44 (0)1908 858787; email ouw-customer-services@open.ac.uk

The Open University
Walton Hall, Milton Keynes
MK7 6AA

First published 2007.

Edited and designed by The Open University.

Typeset by SR Nova Pvt. Ltd, Bangalore, India.

Printed in the United Kingdom by The University Press, Cambridge.

ISBN 978 0 7492 1855 3

1.1

CONTENTS

1 INTRODUCTION

Having looked at a range of failure mechanisms in this block, I'm now going to look at a combination of the fracture mechanics theories you met at the start of the block, paying special attention to the mechanism of failure by yielding.

From Part 1 of this block you should have a clear understanding of the use of the linear-elastic fracture mechanics (LEFM) equation as a means of calculating the conditions for failure of metals in a brittle fashion. Because brittle failure is the most dangerous form of failure, requiring the lowest energy, safety cases for operating plant can be made using LEFM theory even though a failure by crack growth, should it take place, will not be by the flat, brittle fracture processes that the theory requires.

You should also know that a cracked section can fail by plastic collapse, without the crack extending, and that the equations for LEFM and plastic collapse can each be applied to predict failure without either reference to the other or any formal indication of which is relevant. This is an inconvenient state of affairs.

Between the bookends of plastic collapse and LEFM lies the domain of ductile tearing, where crack growth can be slow and is accompanied by relatively large amounts of plasticity compared with the small plastic zone associated with LEFM – this plasticity confers toughness.

When the mechanics crack-driving parameter K equals the materials resistance parameter K_{IC}, fast, brittle fracture takes place. If, however, the plasticity mechanisms resist crack extension and the crack tears by a small amount before stopping, the material toughness is higher. In this case more load, and hence a larger value of the crack-driving parameter, is needed to extend the crack further. This is the field of elastic–plastic fracture mechanics (EPFM).

The theory that underpins EPFM will be considered in this part, but you will not have to use it directly. Rather, I will carry out a set of numerical experiments designed to justify the use of a failure assessment diagram (FAD) of the type used in industry. The beauty of an FAD is that EPFM theory (as well as the benefit of much industrial experience) is implicit in the approach. A large number of engineering crack-assessment problems are dealt with using the same FAD that you will learn to use here. As with the K calculator and the Fatigue calculator, you will use an FAD calculator spreadsheet (called the 'R6 calculator') for routine calculations, once its principles have been understood.

2 FAILURE ASSESSMENT DIAGRAM

I shall first develop the idea of an FAD in its simplest form, using our two existing theories of LEFM and plastic collapse. Then I shall extend the theoretical base of fracture mechanics to EPFM in order to introduce a state-of-the-art FAD, which is just as easy to use as LEFM theory but has a more extensive theoretical and experimental basis.

I shall start by considering a material with a fracture toughness K_{IC} of 80 MPa $\sqrt{m}$ and a yield stress σ_{yield} of 500 MPa, loaded as an edge-cracked plate of cross section 30 mm × 30 mm, in tension. The crack is measured as being 6 mm long.

Figure 5.1 shows the Y calibration for this geometry, which is also accessible in the K calculator.

EXERCISE 5.1

Use LEFM to estimate the load at which brittle fracture takes place. Either do the calculation longhand or use the K calculator.

Reflect on the validity of the result that you obtained in Exercise 5.1. The stress at which this brittle, fast fracture takes place is about 425 MPa, which is close to the yield stress of the material. However, the section is 20% cracked through, so we should consider the plastic collapse load, which is easily calculated on the basis of the net section yielding.

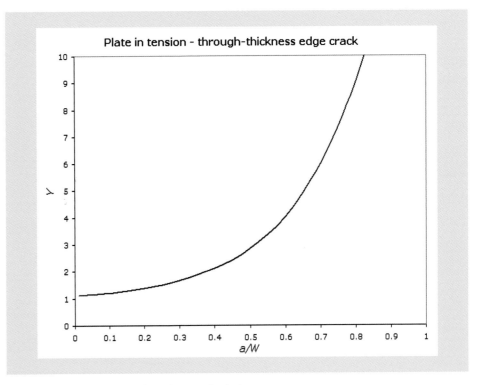

Figure 5.1 Y calibration for edge-cracked plate

Putting the yield stress of 500 MPa across the ligament (i.e. the effective remaining cross-sectional area of the plate) gives a load of 500 MPa × 0.024 m × 0.03 m, which is 360 kN. This is less than the brittle fracture load of 383 kN calculated in Exercise 5.1. In other words, we have been happily calculating a brittle failure load when our other theory has already predicted failure by plastic collapse.

So, our two simple theories are orthogonal: they treat the two material properties as being independent for any particular section. They are extremes of failure behaviour that do not, in themselves, define their sphere of applicability, and so the practitioner – you – can apply either one inappropriately.

This exercise can be represented in an FAD by plotting K normalized by K_{IC} against σ normalized by σ_{yield}. This gives the box diagram shown in Figure 5.2.

Brittle failure occurs when $K = K_{IC}$, so the ratio K/K_{IC} cannot exceed 1. Similarly, failure by yield occurs when $\sigma = \sigma_{yield}$, so the ratio σ/σ_{yield} cannot exceed 1. These limiting conditions create an envelope (marked by the solid line) within which any coordinate point (σ/σ_{yield}, K/K_{IC}) calculated using the LEFM and plastic collapse theories for a cracked part is 'safe', in that it has not reached one of the two limiting conditions. As σ changes, so does K; so if the load is increased or decreased, the coordinate point is driven up and down the dotted line from the origin.

I have chosen the part geometry for the assessment point plotted in Figure 5.2 so that the associated line goes through the junction of the two limiting conditions, in order to emphasize the independence of the two theories. Plastic collapse and brittle failure are predicted to occur simultaneously! Nevertheless, this FAD represents the application of the two theories in a very accessible way.

Another part geometry might produce a coordinate point that, under increasing load, would intersect the plastic collapse limiting condition fairly and squarely, as

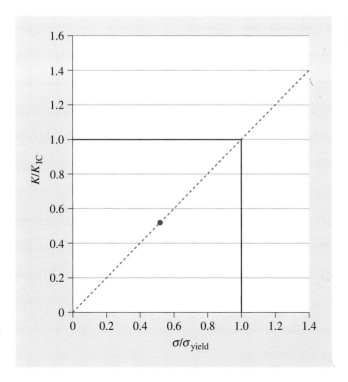

Figure 5.2 A failure envelope

shown in Figure 5.3. In this case the failure might well occur due to plastic collapse. Equally, a third part geometry might produce a coordinate point that would intersect the brittle fracture limiting condition under increasing load (Figure 5.4), in which case the failure might well occur by brittle, fast fracture mechanisms.

So, if the coordinate point is close to either axis on the diagram it gives the practitioner a good idea of what the failure mode might be in an easily

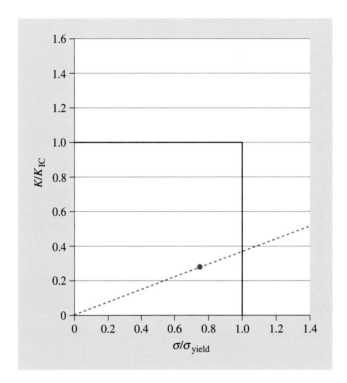

Figure 5.3 Predicted failure by plastic collapse

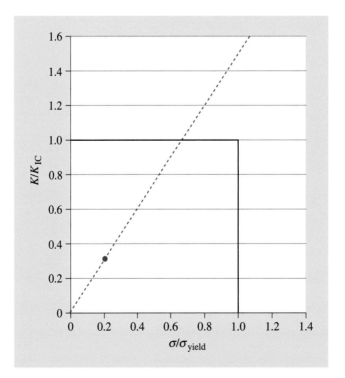

Figure 5.4 Predicted failure by brittle fracture

communicated, pictorial form. The FAD also warns about possible difficulties with the application of both theories, the warning being given by the assessment point heading towards the corner.

An additional benefit of such diagrams is that they give a picture of how far the coordinate, or failure assessment point, is from the failure boundary. This gives a measure of 'safety': if the assessment point is halfway to the boundary then the stress (and hence the load) needs to be doubled in order to reach failure. Clearly, if an assessment point is outside the boundary then failure has already taken place!

Although I have created this particular FAD simply to demonstrate the power of the visualization, the method can be seen in practice. Figure 5.5 is redrawn from British Standard BS 7910 *Guide to methods for assessing the acceptability of flaws in metallic structures*.

On this figure, the K_r axis is K/K_{IC} and my ratio σ/σ_{yield} has been changed to S_r, which is σ/σ_{flow} (the flow stress is the mean of the yield stress and the ultimate tensile stress (UTS), which is used to take into account work hardening). The rectangular envelope has also been shrunk so that the boundaries are at 0.707 (i.e. $1/\sqrt{2}$, for some incomprehensible reason) instead of 1 on the K_r axis and 0.8 instead of 1 on the S_r axis, in order to include a 'safety factor' of some sort.

You can use this FAD to perform a safety case and claim the probity of a British Standard. However, just because this FAD graces BS 7910 does not mean that this approach is at all useful, or used – and it isn't, in this form: engineering practice involves knowing what is not used as well as how to use what is used. So, there will be no exercises or assessment using this form of the FAD.

EXERCISE 5.2

Calculate the flow stress for:

(a) a stainless steel with a yield stress of 280 MPa and a UTS of 520 MPa

(b) an aluminium alloy with a yield stress of 420 MPa and a UTS of 550 MPa.

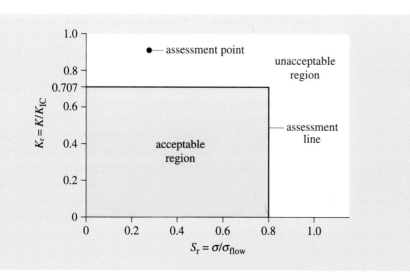

Figure 5.5 FAD redrawn from BS 7910

What you should know from this section:

- That the theories of LEFM and plastic collapse are independent of one another, so one can be used when the other is relevant and vice versa.

- That these two theories can be represented on an FAD.

- That the contents of a British Standard are not necessarily useful or used.

The calculations using LEFM and plastic collapse theories are revision, so you should have had no problems with these.

3 ELASTIC–PLASTIC FRACTURE MECHANICS

In the rectangular FAD the two axes measure the application of the two theories, so an assessment point close to one of the axes gives confidence that a part might fail by the process that the associated theory models. However, a part with an assessment point in the centre – a point that under increased load heads towards the corner, where both theories predict failure – is unlikely to fail by either plastic collapse or brittle fracture.

When a load is applied to a structure, the high (theoretically infinite) stress at the tip causes the tip to blunt and a plastic field to grow. Figure 5.6 shows the LEFM condition where the surrounding elastic field provides all of the crack-driving parameter.

At some point the plasticity at the crack tip becomes large enough to invalidate the assumption of LEFM – that it is the surrounding elastic field that controls the fracture event – and there is an additional plastic contribution to drive the crack. The theory that covers this is EPFM.

First I will consider some physical phenomena, then the theory, followed by the practice.

3.1 Physical events

The striking image shown in Figure 5.7 was made using a scanning electron microscope (SEM) with a depth of focus that allows us to see the whole of the crack front, from the free surface facing us right through to the back surface. The image captures the stage where the blunting of the initially sharp crack has occurred, shown

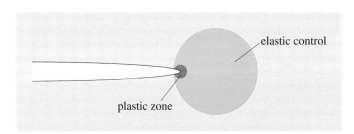

Figure 5.6   In LEFM it is the elastically stressed region that drives crack growth

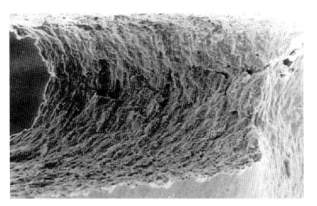

Figure 5.7   SEM image of crack initiation in the blunting zone

by the curvature of the tip. Also, sufficient microstructural damage has taken place in the material ahead of the tip for crack growth to begin, shown by the jagged line along the middle of the blunted surface – this is the EPFM domain.

If the material is tough enough then the crack grows further in a stable fashion, by void coalescence, as the load is increased. Figure 5.8 shows a micrograph of such crack growth in a quenched and tempered steel. The original position of the crack tip is shown by the arrows: it has blunted and then torn stably in an irregular fashion. As it tears, more and more load is required to extend the crack.

The crack in Figure 5.8 is stable and much longer than its initial crack length. The plasticity around this crack is still constrained by the surrounding elastic material; it has not extended to the free surfaces.

What happens next depends critically on how the material hardens and on the geometry that constrains the crack. Figure 5.9 shows the worst possible outcome, which is a small amount of tearing followed by fast, brittle fracture. The regular pattern at the bottom left-hand corner of the picture shows the initial blunting of the

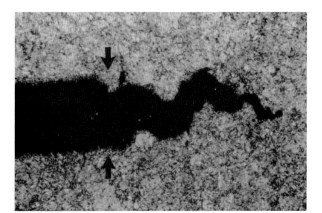

Figure 5.8   Micrograph of crack growth by tearing

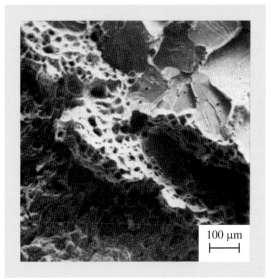

Figure 5.9   SEM image of the change from ductile to brittle failure

100 μm

crack as the load is applied. The band of fracture surface running diagonally from top left to bottom right shows ductile deformation or 'dimpled rupture', produced by ductile tearing under an increasing load. After this short extension the crack is long enough to initiate brittle fracture, which is shown by the cleavage facets in the top right-hand corner of the picture.

At the other end of the spectrum, Figure 5.10 shows a specimen that is tearing slowly through extremely heavily deformed material; plasticity is widespread and has reached the free surfaces.

Figure 5.10 is a tribute to the toughness, and hence utility, of a C–Mn 'mild' steel: after massive deformation and slow crack growth, it's still not in two parts! There is not much interest in, or need for, modelling this complex interaction, as the part's engineering usefulness is long gone.

EXERCISE 5.3

Could you measure a valid K_{IC} for the steel in Figure 5.10?

In other cases between the two possible extremes described above, the crack might grow stably until it was long enough to fail by ductile tearing, with the surface showing little, if any, cleavage.

Whatever the eventual fate of the part, as the crack grows, the most important issue for the engineer is the large increases in toughness that plasticity confers in the very early stages of crack blunting and extension, which need to be accounted for in EPFM analysis and measurement.

Of course, all this presupposes that there is a useful theory for EPFM. There is, but it is not as straightforward as LEFM theory.

Figure 5.10 Tearing through heavy plastic deformation

What you should know from this section:

- That an EPFM crack grows by blunting of the tip followed by tearing due to void coalescence.

- That tearing increases toughness.

- That a tearing crack can become long enough to initiate brittle fracture, or continue tearing until plasticity becomes widespread.

- That tearing and brittle fracture show typical fracture surfaces of dimpled rupture and cleavage respectively.

3.2 Elastic–plastic fracture mechanics theory

LEFM theory admits no plastic deformation, and plastic collapse theory models the shape of a material stress–strain curve using only two material properties, the yield stress and the UTS.

In reality, the variety of stress–strain curves is a tribute to the arts of the alloy designer (Figure 5.11). Perhaps unsurprisingly, the behaviour of a metal when it is tearing depends on the detail of the shape of the work-hardening curve. Some metals work-harden steeply and some shallowly, as shown in Figure 5.12.

The work-hardening curve of a metal is modelled by a power-law relationship:

$$\frac{\varepsilon}{\varepsilon_{\text{yield}}} = \left(\frac{\sigma}{\sigma_{\text{yield}}} + \alpha \left(\frac{\sigma}{\sigma_{\text{yield}}} \right)^{n} \right)$$

in order to fit the shape of a curve (Figure 5.13). It is the value of the strain-hardening exponent n that defines the steepness of the curve: the higher the value of n, the less steep the curve and the sharper the bend.

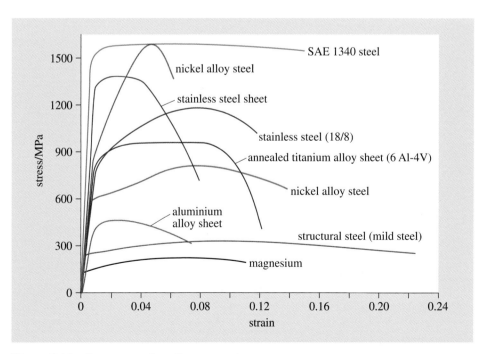

Figure 5.11   Some examples of stress–strain curves

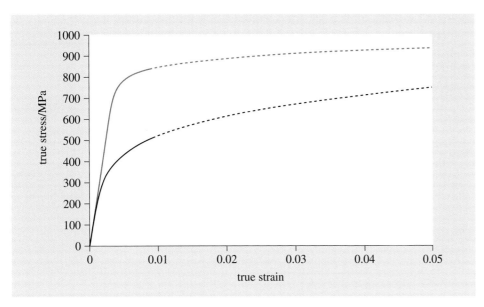

Figure 5.12   Comparison of two different work-hardening behaviours

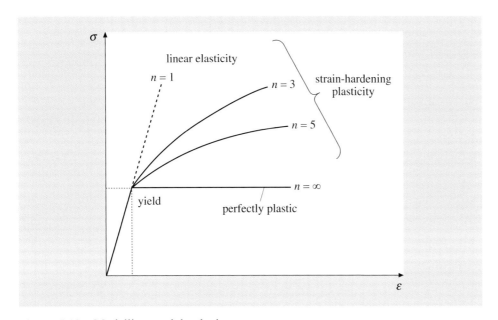

Figure 5.13   Modelling work hardening

For a strongly hardening material n might range between 3 and 5, whereas a gently hardening material might have a value for n as large as 20. A steep work-hardening curve, such as that for an austenitic stainless steel, will throw plasticity ahead of a crack, thus producing a diffuse plastic zone. This is different from a shallow work-hardening curve, which has a plastic zone that is more concentrated at the crack tip.

Once a curve has been given an equation it can be used in theoretical calculations. However, this model of work-hardening behaviour, whilst being non-linear like the real thing, does not simulate the unloading behaviour of a real material. In a real tensile test the load–deflection curve does not follow the same path on unloading after yielding. This model is OK on loading, but on unloading it retraces its steps, so whilst the material response is non-linear it is non-linear elastic. There is no hysteresis loss, or permanent deformation, as there is in a real metal. (Recall the descriptions of cyclic hardening and softening in Part 2, and the descriptions of isotropic and kinematic hardening in Block 1 Part 7: the material does not follow the loading curve on unloading.)

However, this theory is the best available. As with all engineering practice, theory gives us the confidence that we are grouping like with like, and is supported by experiment and experience to cover its shortcomings and enable it to be used with confidence.

3.2.1 Crack-driving parameter J

The starting point for understanding EPFM is that, as with LEFM, there is a characteristic pattern of stresses ahead of a crack tip. Figure 5.14 shows how this pattern varies with angle θ and radius r for two values of material strain-hardening exponent: (a) $n = 3$ and (b) $n = 13$.

Continuing with the description of EPFM theory by analogy, as with the use of K in LEFM there is a crack-tip characterizing parameter for EPFM. In EPFM this is J, which includes non-linearity through n.

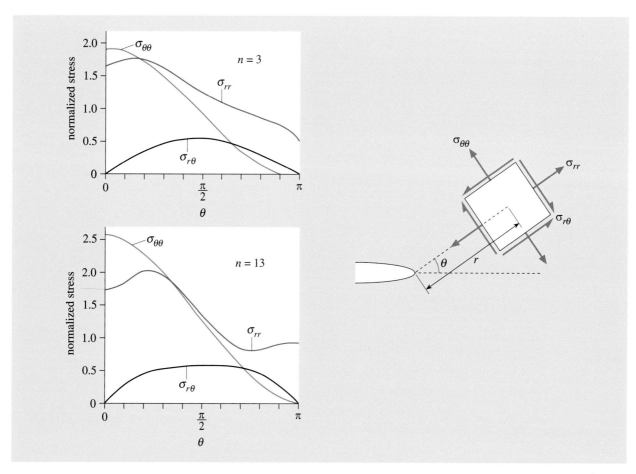

Figure 5.14   EPFM stress variation for different values of n: (a) $n = 3$ and (b) $n = 13$. Here σ represents the stress normalized by the yield stress. The diagram on the right shows the stress components acting on an element ahead of the crack tip, using polar coordinates

EPFM theory describes J as the 'rate of change of net potential energy with respect to crack advance'; think of this as the energy flow into a crack tip. The more energy the crack tip can absorb, the tougher the material and the higher the value of J. A J crack-driving parameter can be thought of in the same way as a K crack-driving parameter: as the load increases, more and more J is fed into the material ahead of the crack.

The J crack-driving parameter consists of an elastic and a plastic component. For an engineer, the conversion between J and K is $J \approx K^2/E$. Using this relationship, $J = J_{elastic} + J_{plastic}$ can be converted to $K = K_{elastic} + K_{plastic}$. In the text I shall use J (or K) to mean the total contribution from both elastic and plastic components, as shown here. However, I shall also use $J_{elastic-plastic}$ where I want to emphasize that J has been obtained by adding an elastic and a plastic component.

So, how do we get a value for J (or its K equivalent)? By using a computer, of course!

J is calculated using a finite element (FE) model of the geometry of a cracked body and an elastic, non-linear representation of the material's stress–strain curve. EPFM theory is limited to small amounts of blunting and tearing, and it is also a static model of a dynamic process. Imagine it as being like the individual frames in a film strip: at each frame the crack is longer and the plasticity is refocused at the crack tip, so in EPFM theory the crack has no wake.

Standard FE packages, such as Abaqus®, incorporate procedures to calculate a J driving force using special crack-tip elements, illustrated in Figure 5.15, as part of its standard toolkit.

Figure 5.16 shows the results from such an FE analysis of a centre-cracked panel under a tensile load. The material is a strongly hardening austenitic stainless steel with a fairly low yield stress – the type that engineers usually call 18/8 stainless (because it typically contains 18% chromium and 8% nickel). This ubiquitous material gains its hardness through deformation, so it is ideal for formable sheet (kitchen sink units are made from it).

The analysis was performed using a standard FE package and J is shown separated into its two components. The solid line is the elastic contribution to J, $J_{elastic}$, the dotted line is the plastic contribution, $J_{plastic}$, and the combination of the two, $J_{elastic-plastic}$, is shown by the dashed line.

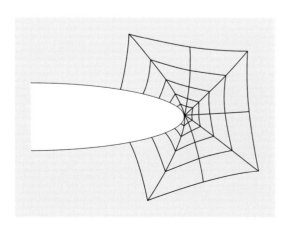

Figure 5.15   Crack-tip elements

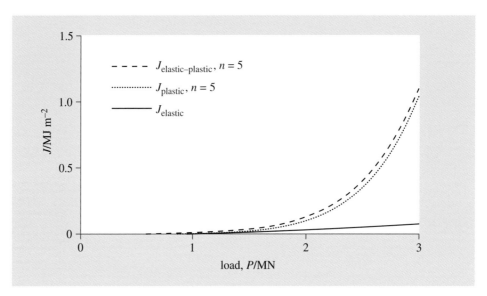

Figure 5.16 $J_{\text{elastic–plastic}} = J_{\text{elastic}} + J_{\text{plastic}}$ for a centre-cracked panel under a tensile load

As the plasticity at the crack tip increases, so the J_{plastic} contribution becomes dominant in the relationship $J_{\text{elastic–plastic}} = J_{\text{elastic}} + J_{\text{plastic}}$. Up until a load of about 1.5 MN on the graph the elastic contribution dominates, but then the plastic contribution to the driving force overwhelms the elastic component.

The solid line in Figure 5.16 could be created directly from an LEFM analysis using the conversion $J_{\text{elastic}} \approx K^2/E$. If we were starting from here we would drop the 'K' terminology and use 'J' exclusively. However, we have to live with historical developments, so what happens is that the plastic J component is also converted into a 'K_{plastic}' using the same formula.

This extends the use of the brittle fracture parameter into the elastic–plastic regime, so is not good terminology – but we have to live with it.

Figure 5.17 shows Figure 5.16 converted into K terminology; this shows the separation between elastic and plastic components rather better.

Such graphs of the two crack-driving parameters in terms of K can be generated for different values of n and different geometries: Figure 5.18 shows the elastic–plastic crack-driving parameters in terms of K for three strain-hardening exponents, $n = 5$, $n = 10$ and $n = 20$, for a beam in four-point bending. These graphs portray vividly the importance of work-hardening rate on the crack-driving parameter.

Clearly, if you have a very complex geometry (such as, say, a welded pipe junction) then you can buy an EPFM analysis for your geometry and material, if you have the budget. Alternatively, there may be standard solutions available for standard geometries.

Once such a mechanics crack-driving parameter is computed, it is matched to a material's resistance parameter. So, as with LEFM fracture toughness ($K = K_{\text{IC}}$), proof stress ($\sigma = \sigma_{0.2}$) and yield stress ($\sigma = \sigma_{\text{yield}}$), we can say that for EPFM the mechanics driving parameter J is increased by loading until it reaches a value at which some physical event is measurable, which we then call J_{material}. How to get such a J_{material} value is the subject of the next section.

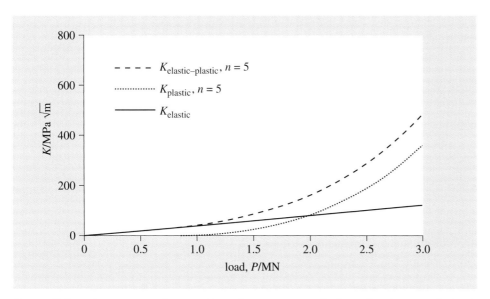

Figure 5.17 $K_{\text{elastic–plastic}} = K_{\text{elastic}} + K_{\text{plastic}}$ for a centre-cracked panel under a tensile load

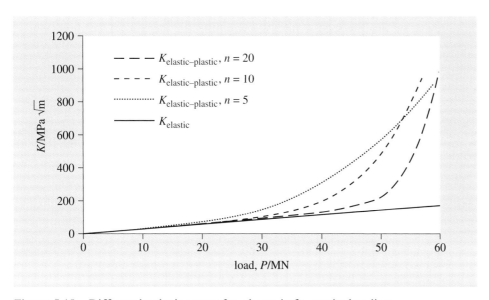

Figure 5.18   Different hardening rates for a beam in four-point bending

What you should know from this section:

- That EPFM depends on the steepness of a material's work-hardening curve, which is defined by the value of n.

- That EPFM theory is non-linear elastic, and it does not model material unloading.

- That J, which has an elastic and a plastic component ($J_{\text{elastic–plastic}} = J_{\text{elastic}} + J_{\text{plastic}}$), is the crack-tip characterizing parameter for EPFM.

- That $J = J_{\text{elastic}} + J_{\text{plastic}}$ can be converted to $K = K_{\text{elastic}} + K_{\text{plastic}}$ using $J \approx K^2/E$.

- That the plastic component of J increases rapidly when there is significant plasticity at the crack tip.

3.2.2 $J_{material}$

A material's property, couched in terms of J and so convertible into K, can be obtained by following the procedures described in British Standards. BS 7448 lays down the methods that a test-house will use to produce a material property for you in exchange for money. However, our concern here is with the principles and some typical values. So, what is $J_{material}$?

A material toughness value that takes into account blunting and tearing at the crack tip in a specimen will be higher than that which characterizes brittle fracture. The measurement that is relevant to EPFM failure is crack extension: engineering judgement specifies that the value of J at an extension of 0.15 mm or 0.2 mm is suitable, depending on your choice of favourite standards.

Measurement techniques described in the standards do not discriminate between blunting and the onset of tearing, so toughness values of $J_{0.2}$ or $J_{0.15}$ contain both mechanisms to a greater or lesser extent. As with crack-driving parameters, they are converted into $K_{material}$ equivalents using $J \approx K^2/E$. Table 5.1 shows some examples of toughness values for a particular steel at different temperatures T.

Table 5.1   Examples of toughness values for A508 pressure-vessel steel

Temperature T	$J_{0.2}$/kJ m^{-2}	$K_{0.2}$/MPa √m
$T < 150\,°C$	120	165
$150\,°C < T < 350\,°C$	105	150

$J_{material}$ values using crack extensions larger than 0.2 mm do appear in industrial documents, but I wouldn't recommend this to ordinary mortals!

DVD

The 'Toughness testing: Corus case study' programme can be found on the course DVD.

I shall now introduce another terminology for toughness after tearing. The course DVD contains an interview that took place at Corus, in which you will hear toughness described in terms of *crack-tip opening displacement*, or CTOD. Although we shall not be using this term in numerical calculations, or in the 'R6 calculator' spreadsheet, it is interesting to know how such terms come into being – and it is important to know this one because it is used at TWI (which used to be The Welding Institute). In many ways, CTOD is the special intellectual property of TWI and the industries that it serves.

If one starts with a clean slate then the issue of what to use as a toughness value for a material and a geometry that tears can be formulated as follows: 'Can one characterize a crack by measuring the force at the loading pins, or does one need to get as close to the crack tip as possible in order to find a suitable crack-tip characterizing parameter?'. Put simply, J is measured at the loading pins, whereas CTOD is measured at the mouth of the crack (Figure 5.19), which is as close to the tip as it is practical to approach. If both methods are appropriate then J, and its K equivalent, ought to be related to CTOD. And indeed, here is the relationship:

$$\delta = \frac{1}{m\sigma_{yield}} J = \frac{1}{m\sigma_{yield}} \frac{K^2}{E}$$

where δ is the displacement and m, which is about 2 in plane strain, is the fudge factor (or, more officially, a dimensionless constant that depends on the material properties and the stress states!).

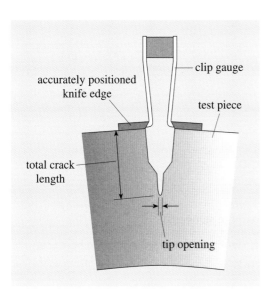

Figure 5.19 Measuring CTOD in a toughness test

clip gauge

accurately positioned
knife edge

test piece

total crack
length

tip opening

It is clearly much easier to measure an effect at the loading pins of a testing machine, so the use of J (or its K terminology equivalent) should have come to dominate the field. However, pipeline and offshore industries have a huge investment in a body of knowledge using CTOD, which pre-dated J by many years. So, if you deal with this industrial sector then you may have to be familiar with the terminologies of CTOD, which come from the PhD thesis of Alan Wells, later to become Director General of TWI. If you work in the aircraft industries or the nuclear industries, or indeed if you work outside the UK, you will not see much, if anything, of this terminology.

In this part, I shall use $K_{material}$ values of $K_{0.2}$ for material toughness in the EPFM region as the norm.

What you should know from this section:

- That a value of $J_{material}$ can be defined when some observable physical event occurs.

- That this $J_{material}$ can be converted into a $K_{material}$ using $J \approx K^2/E$.

- That British Standards define this physical event as a crack growth – that combines blunting and tearing – of, say, 0.2 mm.

- That a material toughness of $J_{material} = J_{0.2}$ can be converted into a value of $K_{0.2}$ using $J \approx K^2/E$.

- That pipeline and offshore industries use CTOD as a measure of toughness.

3.3 Practical guidance

There is a lot of confusion about what value and type of toughness to use when conducting safety cases and analysing problems, so here are some useful guidelines:

- Austenitic (often stainless) and workaday ferritic steels on the ductile upper shelf will not fail in a brittle manner at humanly achievable sizes. Such metals tear, so use $K_{0.2}$ values (which can easily be over 100 MPa √m).

- Older steels on the lower shelf at normal operating temperatures will fail by fast brittle fracture at fracture toughnesses as low as $K_{IC} = 40$ MPa √m, so check for LEFM failure.

- Ferritic steels in the transition region are ambiguous: the same material in small sizes can tear appreciably before failing, but in large sizes it can fail by brittle, fast fracture. So, consider both possibilities when conducting safety cases.

- If you are designing safety-critical kit, make sure that steels are on the upper shelf under normal operating conditions. Note that plant operating at high temperatures might be subject to cold temperatures during emergency procedures, which is a particular problem for the nuclear power-plant industry.

Working with an EPFM analysis from the ground up can be an expensive business. To turn these ideas into a practical engineering tool requires the results of numerical analyses to be presented in the context of practical experience. The solution is an FAD that works in the same way as the one in Figure 5.5 but, in addition, incorporates EPFM principles.

What you should know from this section:

- That austenitic steels and ferritic steels on the upper shelf are tough, but ferritic steels on the lower shelf can have comparatively low values of toughness.

4 DEVELOPING A FAILURE ASSESSMENT DIAGRAM

4.1 Creating a failure assessment diagram for a steel beam

An FAD with the simplicity and straightforwardness of Figure 5.5, but that takes into account tearing, has evolved over a period of about 20 years of theoretical development and engineering practice. Using this engineering curve – which is an industry standard – a failure case can be made without the need for a specific EPFM analysis, as this is implicit in the diagram. In this section I shall show how an FAD can be created, using the results of some numerical analyses that I have produced to demonstrate the principles. In the first instance I shall develop an FAD for one particular case: that of a bending specimen in a moderately hardening material. Then, afterwards, I shall show how this is generalized. Note that I shall use K terminology from now on.

Figure 5.20 shows the results of an FE analysis for a four-point bending specimen. The crack-driving parameter $K_{\text{elastic–plastic}}$ is shown plotted against the applied load P normalized by its plastic collapse load P_{L} (this is also known as the limit load, L_{r}). The hardening exponent n for the material is 10.

The limit load is the failure load at which the ligament of our cracked beam becomes fully plastic and so forms a hinge (plastic collapse) – it becomes a mechanism rather than a structure.

At first sight, this should mean that the ratio of P/P_{L} shouldn't exceed 1. However, this limit load is calculated using the yield stress of the material, which is a lower-bound value because, after yield, the material work-hardens, which increases its load-carrying capacity. So, in practice, load ratios greater than 1 are possible.

Whereas in previous parts F has been used to represent a force, this part uses P when describing applied loads (as opposed to p, which represents a pressure). Both F and P are common symbols used to represent load and force.

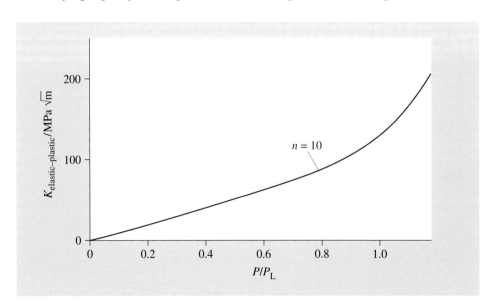

Figure 5.20   Elastic–plastic crack-driving parameter in four-point bending

To generalize the curve, I now want to normalize the K axis. If this is plotted as $K_{elastic}/K_{elastic-plastic}$ then it performs the neat trick of inverting the curve, to form an envelope (Figure 5.21).

The extreme of L_r (P/P_L) can be cut off by the ratio of flow stress to yield stress in order to limit the diagram if failure is by plastic collapse (Figure 5.22). For example, take a material with a UTS of 800 MPa and a yield strength of 600 MPa. The normalized load axis cannot exceed the flow stress divided by the yield stress:

$$\frac{\frac{1}{2}\left(800\ \text{MPa} + 600\ \text{MPa}\right)}{600\ \text{MPa}} \approx 1.17$$

The curve would, therefore, be limited by this value. The normalized driving-force curve would go on forever without this cut-off line.

If there were no plastic crack-driving force then the vertical axis would be fixed at 1, giving the box diagram (shown by the dotted lines in Figure 5.23). The box is effectively Figure 5.5, without the so-called safety factors incorporated.

The curve is a mechanics curve for a four-point bending specimen in a material with known plasticity characteristics (hardening exponent, yield and ultimate stresses), which starts at 1 and falls as plasticity reduces the load-carrying capacity until the load at which plastic collapse takes place is reached.

Now consider plotting the situation where the beam experiences a $K_{elastic}$ as a result of an applied load P. These values are normalized to the values of $K_{material}$ and P_L, and the assessment point would then be represented by the coordinate

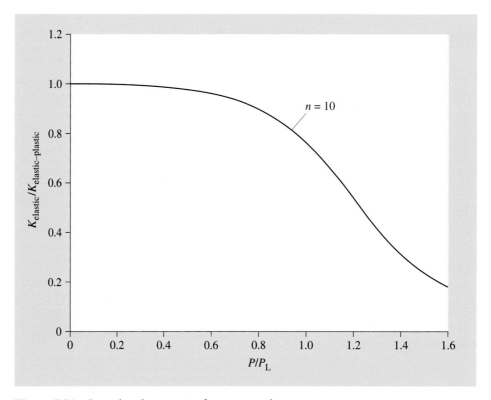

Figure 5.21   Inverting the curve to form an envelope

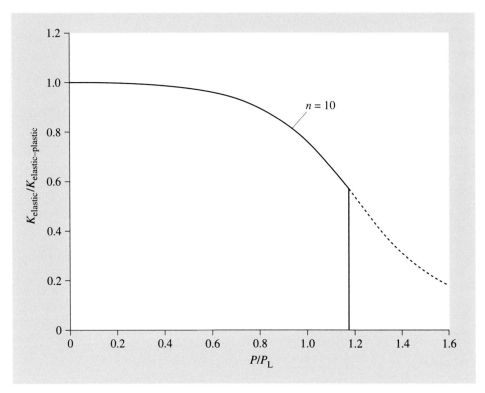

Figure 5.22   Cut-off line applied to the curve

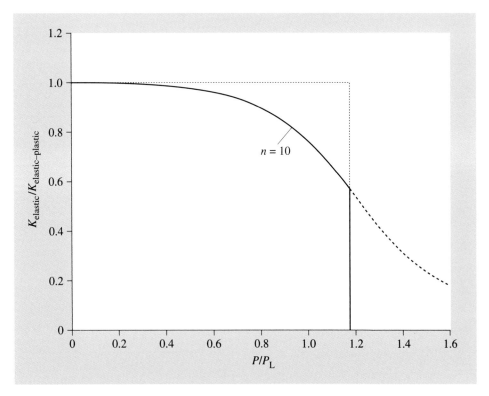

Figure 5.23   The curve without the plastic crack-driving force would be the box diagram

$(L_r, K_r) = (P/P_L, K_{elastic}/K_{material})$ shown circled in Figure 5.24. It lies inside the envelope (below the curve), so the mechanics driving parameter and the materials resistance parameter do not match, and thus the beam is safe.

Now imagine that I can vary the material toughness at will without altering any other material properties. If I increase the material's toughness then the assessment point moves down, and if I reduce the toughness then the point will move up – as shown in the figure. When I have reduced the toughness enough, the material's assessment point coincides with the mechanics driving curve and failure is predicted.

SAQ 5.1 (Learning outcome 5.1)

What measures of material toughness, $K_{material}$, can be implemented for use in failure assessments?

Now consider what would happen to each of the assessment points shown in Figure 5.25 if the load on the beam were varied. If the load is changed, then $K_{elastic}$ varies with P and so K_r and L_r change equally. This means that as the load increases or decreases, each assessment point traces a path to and from the origin, as shown in the figure. As long as a point lies within the envelope then the corresponding part is still, to a greater or lesser extent, 'safe'.

When an assessment point reaches the boundary curve, failure is predicted – but in different ways for the three points. The low-toughness line intersects with the curve in an area that predicts brittle fracture. The high-toughness line suggests failure by plastic collapse, and the medium-toughness line by tearing – it is in the EPFM region.

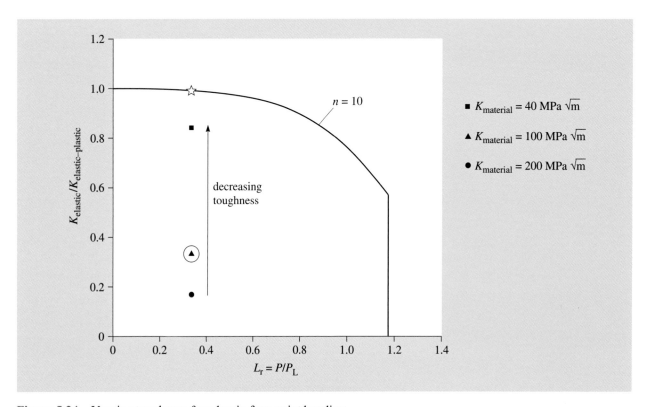

Figure 5.24   Varying toughness for a bar in four-point bending

So, in each case the FAD conveys information about the type of failure and gives a picture of the nearness of approach to failure (Figure 5.26 – the reserve factor on load is OB/OA).

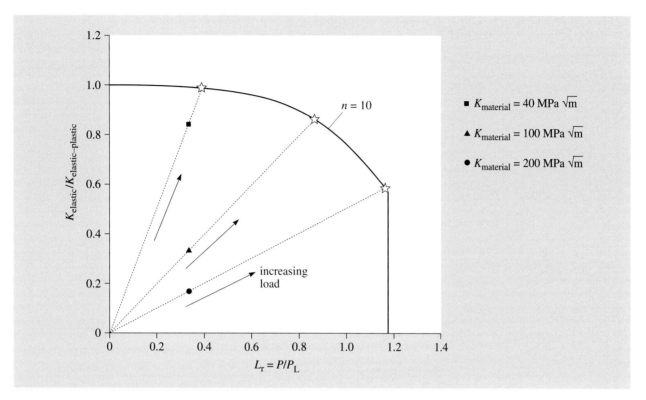

Figure 5.25   Plotting variation with load

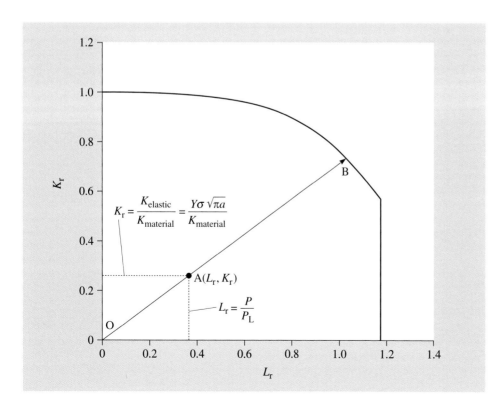

Figure 5.26   Assessment point on FAD: the reserve factor on load is OB/OA

It is worth portraying the results of an analysis that is bought and paid for in this way, because it is a good way of communicating the analysis and the effect of various uncertainties. For example, these calculations were all performed with one crack length, but the sensitivity of the assessment point to change in crack length, or some other unknown, is easily portrayed.

Our FE analysis is that of a beam specimen in four-point bending made from one specific material. Individual analyses are expensive, so what is required for practical engineering problems is an engineering FAD with a curve that will be generally lower than other specific curves (and therefore conservative) for different geometries and hardening characteristics. This will be useful only if the curves for different geometries and material-hardening characteristics tend to group together. So, let's find out whether they do.

4.2 Generalizing the failure assessment diagram

To create a general curve I need to consider both variations in materials and variations in geometries.

Figure 5.27 shows representative curve-fitted, work-hardening curves for a range of materials:

- The material with $n = 5$ is most like an austenitic stainless steel such as AISI 304, the ubiquitous 18/8 stainless, which yields at about 200 MPa and hardens to about 500 MPa during forming.

- The material with $n = 10$ is like a high-strength, ferritic, pressure-vessel steel, which typically has a yield stress of 600 MPa. It is representative of A508 grade 4N,

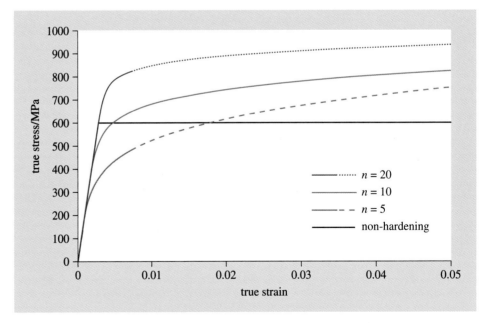

Figure 5.27   Curve-fitted, work-hardening curves for various materials

which is a candidate material for high-strength forgings in the nuclear industry.

- The material with $n = 20$ is roughly like a heat-treated and tempered, medium-carbon, high-strength, low-alloy steel such as AISI 4140, which is used for axles, gears, bolts and connecting rods in the automotive and aircraft industries for components where both high strength and high toughness are important.

Figure 5.28 shows the FE results for these three materials as individual failure assessment curves. This is most encouraging because, despite the widely different responses, the three envelopes group nicely together in the EPFM region. One can easily imagine a single curve that represents a useful engineering curve. Note that all three curves will have different cut-off points for plastic collapse.

Figure 5.29 shows these three curves with the industry-standard engineering curve (labelled R6) added as a solid line. This curve is a simple polynomial equation chosen on the basis of engineering judgement and experience. Its full name is the R6 Revision 4 Option 1 curve, or Option 1 curve for short (engineers aren't very good at names!). That it is Revision 4 is a tribute to its longevity – and it is not all that different from the curve for Revision 3, which gives added confidence. The fact that this curve is Option 1 shows that it is a first step: there are other options that are more materials specific, but they need not concern us here.

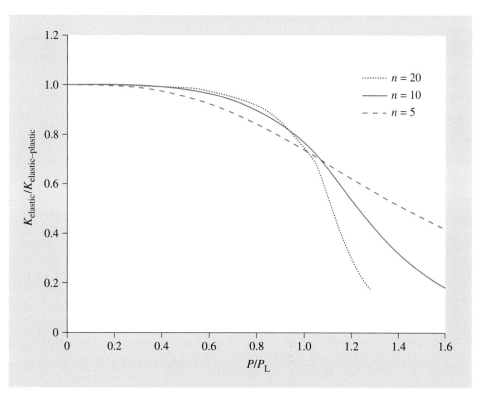

Figure 5.28   Failure assessment curves for the three materials from Figure 5.27, in four-point bending

So much for the different hardening behaviours. What about different geometries: do they group together?

Curves for the same materials loaded as centre-cracked tension (CCT) panels are shown superimposed over the R6 Option 1 curve in Figure 5.30.

Figure 5.29   The three failure assessment curves with the R6 curve added

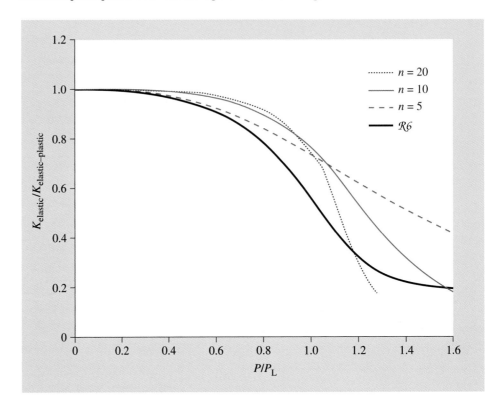

Figure 5.30   Results for the same materials loaded as CCT panels

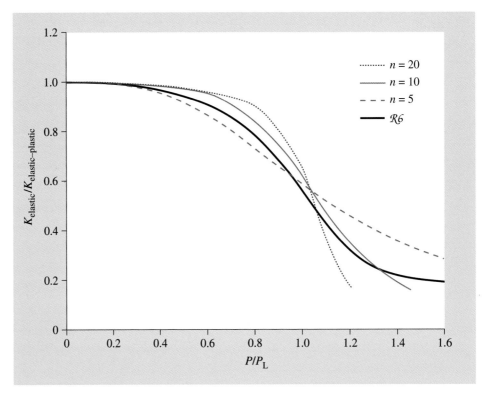

A CCT panel has all the material ahead of the crack tip in tension, whereas a bending specimen has a compressive stress ahead of the tensile field in front of the crack. The 'constraint' is very different in the two cases, and yet the Option 1 curve is still a good engineering generalization.

Laboratory specimens are all very well, but this justification needs to be tried on a practical, complex geometry. The image shown in Figure 5.31 demonstrates the common problem of a nozzle-to-cylinder intersection. The results of analysing the three differently hardening materials for this geometry are shown in Figure 5.32, which again shows that the Option 1 curve is a good engineering approximation.

This is something of an impressive collection: three widely different materials in three very different geometries cluster together around the industry-standard curve (Figure 5.33).

Figure 5.31 Nozzles on a pressure vessel: the common problem of a nozzle-to-cylinder intersection

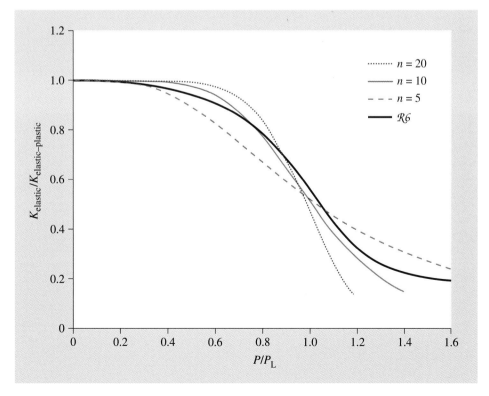

Figure 5.32 Results for the three materials for the nozzle-to-cylinder geometry

- .... $n = 20$
- —— $n = 10$
- – – – $n = 5$
- —— $R6$

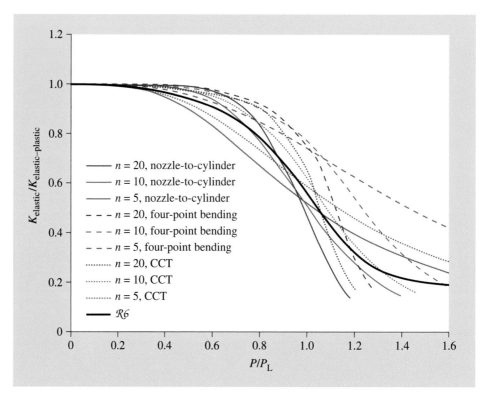

Figure 5.33   All the results for the different materials and geometries

The R6 curve has had far more justification in its 20-year lifetime than I have been able to show here, and many people have contributed to its development. So, the Option 1 solid line captures the best of engineering analysis and experience in the form of a single curve, which is accessible to all of us at no cost. Unless, that is, you buy it captured in very expensive, validated software.

In essence, EPFM theory is implicit in the Option 1 curve, which is also part of BS 7910, so this is the FAD to use.

What you should know from this section:

- That there is a single general engineering curve, 'R6 Option 1', that describes the sum of the elastic and plastic crack-driving parameters from LEFM through EPFM to plastic collapse for a range of geometries and strain-hardening exponents.

- How to calculate the cut-off position using yield and UTS.

- How to plot a material assessment point on the FAD.

- How such an assessment point will vary with toughness and load – and that when the assessment point meets the curve, failure will be predicted.

- How to calculate a reserve factor on load by measuring from the diagram.

5 STEPS IN USING R6

In this section you will follow through the steps of an R6 assessment longhand and check that your calculation is the same as that of the R6 calculator.

Step 1

The starting point of a failure assessment is always the general failure assessment curve (Figure 5.34 overleaf).

Step 2

Put in a cut-off that depends on the flow stress of the material as:

$$L_r = \frac{\sigma_{flow}}{\sigma_{yield}}$$

SAQ 5.2 (Learning outcome 5.2)

A pressurized, welded pipe with a mean diameter of 240 mm and a wall thickness of 10 mm (it is valid to assume that this is thin-walled and so the hoop stresses are constant over the wall thickness) is made from a steel with a yield stress of 400 MPa, a UTS of 500 MPa and a Charpy toughness, C_v, of 15 J. It is designed to operate at 15 MPa.

Calculate the R6 cut-off line and draw it on your diagram.

Step 3

Calculate the K_r coordinate of an assessment point for a specific problem.

To do this requires the calculation of the elastic crack-driving force using LEFM theory:

$$K = Y\sigma\sqrt{\pi a}$$

The ratio of K to $K_{material}$ is K_r, which requires a judgement about the appropriate material toughness for the problem. Using K_{IC} for $K_{material}$ is the usual starting point, as it is the lowest and, therefore, the most conservative toughness value. It is also the easiest and cheapest to obtain, and if a safety case using K_{IC} is valid then further refinement is not necessary.

SAQ 5.3 (Part 1 revision)

The pipe from SAQ 5.2 contains a long, surface-breaking, axial edge crack 1 mm deep on its inside surface. Calculate the K_r coordinate of an assessment point. You can ignore the radius of the pipe to calculate K and so use an edge-cracked plate Y calibration factor.

You will need to use the SINTAP recommendation from Block 2 Part 1 that relates K_{IC} to Charpy toughness: $K_{IC} = 12C_v^{0.5}$.

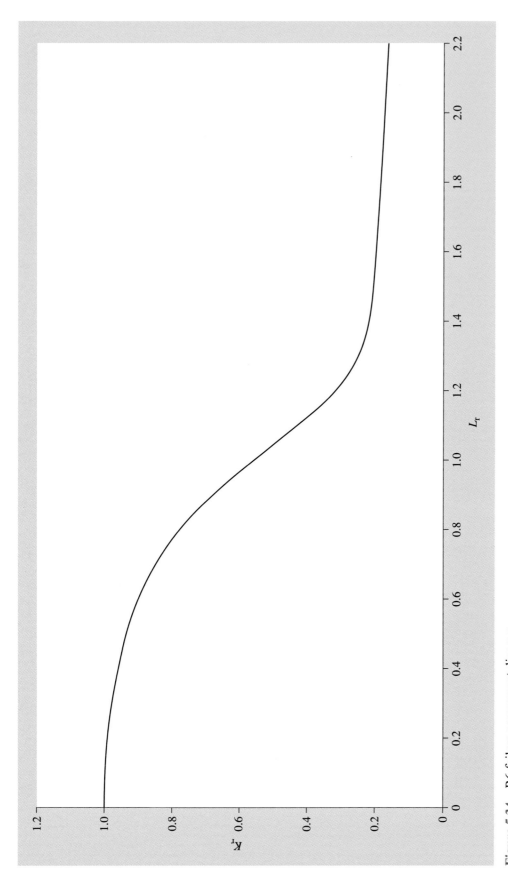

Figure 5.34   R6 failure assessment diagram

Step 4

Calculate L_r using the ratio of the applied load to the load at which plastic collapse occurs (found using the yield stress of the material).

SAQ 5.4 (Learning outcome 5.3)

Calculate L_r for the pipe. The applied pressure, p, is 15 MPa. The pressure to cause plastic collapse, p_L, is that required to cause yield over the ligament, which is equivalent to a wall thickness of 9 mm.

Step 5

Plot the assessment point (L_r, K_r).

The assessment point is shown in Figure 5.35. Ensure that you are happy with how the data points have been calculated.

Step 6

Extend the assessment-point line until it intersects with the curve (Figure 5.36) and calculate the reserve factor on load. (Remember that the reserve factor on load is given by the length from the origin to the curve intersection divided by the length from the origin to the assessment point.)

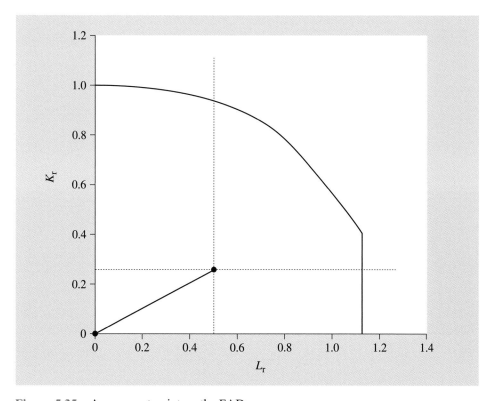

Figure 5.35   Assessment point on the FAD

Figure 5.36
Assessment-point line
extended to intersect with
curve

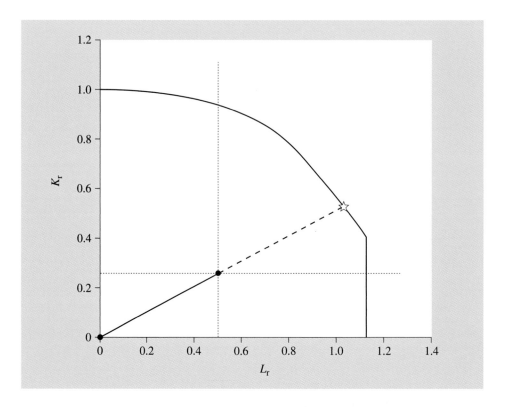

SAQ 5.5 (Learning outcome 5.4)

Measure the reserve on load from your diagram.

EXERCISE 5.4

What does the FAD suggest is the likely mode of failure?

DVD

The 'R6 calculator'
spreadsheet can be
found on the course
DVD. Instructions on
using it are given in the
Study Guide included
with this mailing.

SAQ 5.6 (Learning outcome 5.5)

Check the longhand solution with the R6 calculator solution. As mentioned
in SAQ 5.3, you can ignore the radius of the pipe and so use the edge-cracked
plate geometry. Don't forget to hit 'Calculate' each time you change the values.

The stress due to the design pressure should be entered in the 'Primary stress'
box. For now, you should leave the 'Secondary stress' box empty; you will
look at secondary stresses in Section 6.

What you should know from this section:

- The procedure for producing an FAD and an assessment point for a particular
  geometry and material.

- How to determine the reserve factor on load.

- How to use the R6 calculator.

6 RESIDUAL STRESSES

A significant issue in the use of FADs over the years has been the treatment of residual stresses. Residual stress is an example of a secondary stress – another example might be thermal shock loads. Here, I shall illustrate the problem by considering local stresses introduced during welding, which are by far the most important.

Welding is a form of local casting by melting and filling between neighbouring, solid metal. When the weld metal solidifies, it contracts, thus setting up local stresses around the weld. These stresses must be in local equilibrium, so some will be tensile and some will be compressive. We covered this in detail in Block 1 Part 7.

Cast weld metal and the neighbouring heat-affected zone (HAZ) will have different material properties from the surrounding, forged, parent plate, and the welding process is also very good at introducing flaws. When these flaws, perhaps in material with reduced toughness, coincide with residual stresses that combine with loading stresses to open a crack, the results can be disastrous. Conservative assumptions for creating a safety case would demand that the flaw and the stresses are all oriented to produce the worst possible case.

There are two major problems in dealing with residual stresses: the first problem lies in knowing their values and the second concerns what happens to them in the presence of local plasticity.

Residual stresses in the body of a metal are difficult and expensive to measure, and hard to eliminate. Best practice demands pre- and post-weld heat treatments to reduce the propensity for introducing stresses and also to ameliorate the magnitude of those introduced. In thick sections it is next to impossible to eliminate residual welding stresses completely. The ballpark figures for the remaining residual stresses in a pre- and post-weld heat-treated vessel are about 20% of yield, and for a vessel without treatment they are about 80% of yield.

However, conservative failure assessment procedures often require the starting assumption of residual stresses at yield, and measurements of residual stresses above yield have been made in some very highly constrained geometries. These are very high values of stress when compared with a high value for load-induced design stress of two-thirds yield for a loaded structure.

It is local plasticity during shakedown and proof loading that is relied on to 'wash out' self-equilibrating residual stresses, but how much residual stress has been washed out and how much remains at some lower value of load?

What follows is the simplest way to treat the problem.

If a failure mode is going to be brittle, then the secondary stress can be considered to act on the flaw as if it were a load-induced design stress. However, as the load increases to, say, a significant proportion of the plastic collapse load, the effect of the secondary stress driving forces becomes less and less because they are relaxed by local plasticity.

So, the easiest way to model this is to assume that the secondary stress contributes only to the K_r axis, as:

$$K_r = \frac{Y\sigma_{primary}\sqrt{\pi a}}{K_{material}} + \frac{Y\sigma_{secondary}\sqrt{\pi a}}{K_{material}}$$

The term 'secondary' is used to distinguish other kinds of stress from the 'primary' stress caused by applied loads or pressure.

The effect of this assumption about the way that the residual stress acts has been to move the load line up the K_r axis, as shown in Figure 5.37. All other ways in which the R6 diagram is used are the same.

SAQ 5.7 (Learning outcome 5.6)

Produce FADs for the pipe you looked at in Section 5, using residual welding stresses of 20%, 80% and 100% of yield. If you use the R6 calculator, note that residual stresses are entered in the 'Secondary stress' box.

With diagrams such as those you produced in SAQ 5.7, you can picture clearly the effect of different realities and assumptions about the values of residual stress: the reserve factor on load comes crashing down as residual stress increases.

Let's assume that your pipe has been automatically welded with high-quality pre- and post-weld heat treatment, so you choose to do the assessment with 20% of yield as a residual stress and now need to consider what would be the effect of an increase in crack length due to fatigue.

EXERCISE 5.5

Gradually increase the crack length until the FAD indicates failure. At what crack length does this occur?

Note: you'll have to do this manually in the calculator, recalculating the assessment point each time with the new crack length.

Figure 5.37   The effect of residual stresses

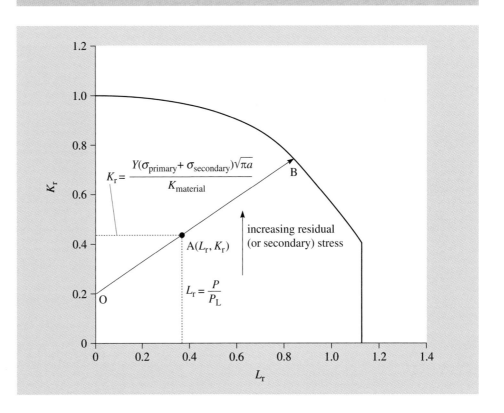

The results of Exercise 5.5 can be shown on a *sensitivity diagram* (Figure 5.38). This shows that the reserve factor falls very rapidly as the crack length increases; a shallower fall would be much better, indicating less sensitivity of the value of the reserve to the crack length. Such sensitivity diagrams can be plotted for any variation of critical variables.

Imagine that all the variables can be altered independently. Varying the different parameters moves the failure assessment point as shown in Figure 5.39.

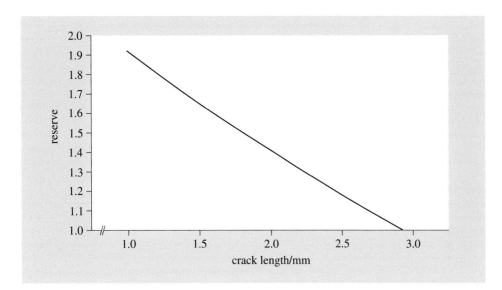

Figure 5.38   Sensitivity diagram

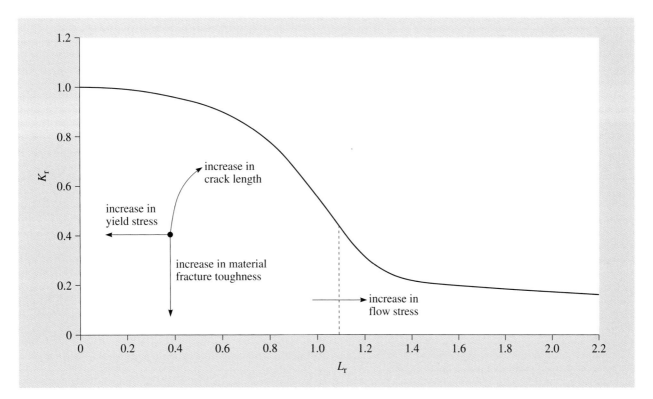

Figure 5.39   Moving the assessment point around

EXERCISE 5.6

Increasing the yield stress drives the assessment point to the left, as shown in Figure 5.39. What other effect would an increase in yield stress have on the plot?

What you should know from this section:

- How to represent secondary stresses, such as residual welding stresses, on an FAD.

- How to plot a sensitivity diagram.

7 CRACKS IN SERVICE

The cracks we have dealt with so far have been the regular cracks that are introduced into test pieces by controlled initiation and loadings, but service cracks are not so obliging. Figure 5.40 shows a triangular, light-coloured facet that caused brittle fracture of the pressure vessel shown in Figure 5.41 under proof testing.

Standards provide advice on how to turn complicated shapes into geometries for which solutions are available, and how to treat cracks that are close to other cracks. Take the flaw in Figure 5.40 by way of an example; this could be modelled as a circular embedded flaw (for which there are handbook solutions) that encompasses the triangle.

In this section I am going to look at a practical problem using a geometry that is commonly found in practice. The problem to be dealt with is numerous incidents of cracking in deaerators, particularly in the USA, that caused catastrophic failures.

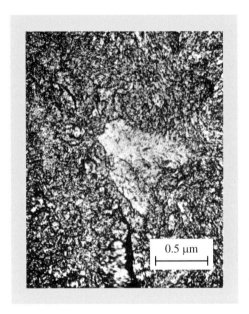

Figure 5.40 Triangular flaw viewed using a light microscope

0.5 μm

Figure 5.41 Pressure vessel that failed under proof testing

Deaerators are pressure vessels that remove air from the feedwater for boilers in order to reduce corrosion. This type of kit comes in all shapes and sizes, and is operated in different regulatory regimes and under different industrial customs and practices, from paper mills to nuclear power stations. Figure 5.42 shows a large and complicated boiler system that includes a deaerator.

As a result of fatalities and litigation, the problem attained a high profile in the news (see ☑ **Concern rises for safety of feedwater deaerators** ☑) and so the company responsible for legislation in the UK was asked, by its insurers, to implement an inspection programme. It was known that cracks in this plant grow by corrosion fatigue, and that cracks around welds and in the HAZs are very common.

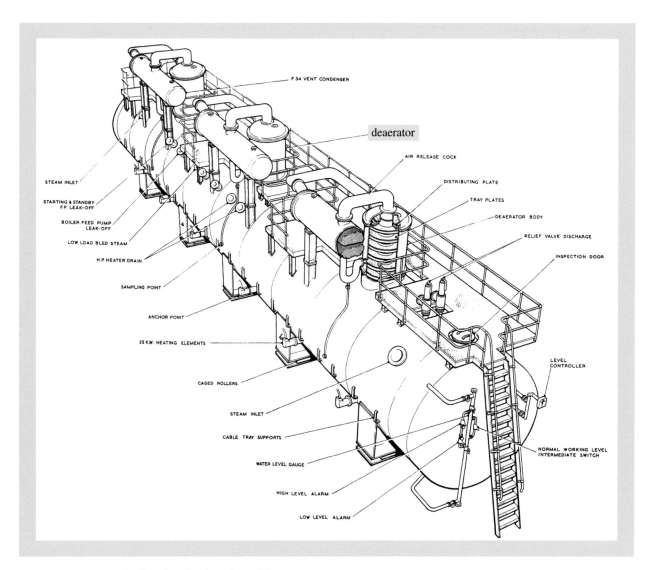

Figure 5.42   Large boiler showing location of deaerator

▽ Concern rises for safety of feedwater deaerators

The following text is taken from a 1983 article published in POWER, a US industry magazine based in Houston, Texas, at a time when deaerator failures were becoming an increasing problem.

Discovery of widespread DA weld cracks in the wake of failures focuses attention anew on inspection and welding procedures.

A flurry of inspection activity in steam-plant operations of the pulp and paper industry, precipitated by the deaerator failure at a Pine Hill (Ala) plant last January and two subsequent storage-vessel ruptures, has uncovered a surprising incidence of deaerator-weld cracking around the country. The rising concern for safety has led the Technical Assn of the Pulp & Paper Industry (Tappi) to issue an advisory alerting its membership to the situation, urging immediate non-destructive examination (NDE) of all DA welds, both in the heater and storage sections.

Deaerator problems have been recognized for some time, both here and abroad. British Columbia's provincial Boiler & Pressure Vessel Safety Branch has kept tabs on the occurrence of implosions and reported incidents of weld cracking in that province for several years. It issued an advisory last July, recommending inspection of all feedwater storage tanks in service for three years or longer. The advisory was sent to all plants (at hospitals, saw mills, paper mills, and elsewhere) with boilers producing at least 1 000 000 lb/hr of steam.

Pulp and paper manufacture is not the only industry reporting such incidents. Law Engineering Co reports that they have occurred at rubber-tire-manufacturing plants, where deaerating units are smaller but operate at higher pressures. The firm's investigators have found extensive cracking in nozzles and nozzle welds, both in these units and in the much larger ones used (at lower operating pressures) at paper mills, the cracks occurring in the circumferential nozzle weld and even radiating out into the base material.

At paper mills, as pointed out by Industrial NDT Co, particular attention during inspection is being given to the circumferential head-to-shell weld, since that appears to be the point of failure in the three incidents cited by Tappi.

The Tappi action was prompted by both the Canadian experience and events in this country. Distributed last month following deliberations of its Deaerator Task Group at the National Meeting in Dallas, the alert reported that cracks had been discovered in the weld material or heat-affected zones of at least 68 vessels – more than half of those inspected this year. Cracking is both longitudinal and transverse to the seams [see Figure 5.43].

Attributed primarily to corrosion fatigue, cracking apparently cannot be correlated with manufacturer, pressure, size, age, capacity, or

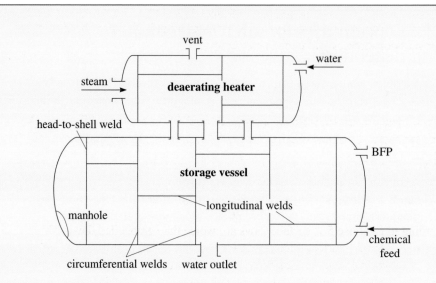

Figure 5.43 Welds are source of deaerator problems [redrawn from original article]

feedwater treatment. Tappi points out the DA vessels can be properly inspected only from inside and that wet-fluorescent magnetic-particle examination is the only NDE method considered effective. While 100% inspection of all circumferential, longitudinal, and nozzle welds is preferred, inspection of 20% of each weld is considered a minimum. External support and structural welds are to be included, and random testing should be done over the full extent of each weld. While this applies to all welds, special emphasis is placed on head-to-shell welds and those lying below the water line.

To ensure proper surface preparations, Tappi says it is essential to grind inspection areas to a smooth finish – possibly flush with the base metal. Weld undercutting or corrosion should be removed, and care should be taken that grinding does not mask relevant indications. If cracking is detected at any point, the particular inspection should be expanded to determine the extent and severity of the crack. Additional magnetic-particle testing may be dictated, as well as radiography or other inspection techniques. Applicable rules of the National Boiler & Pressure Vessel Inspectors … should serve as the guide for repairs.

Here, I shall follow the issues and analyses covered by a panel of experts, the Deaerator Inspection Working Group, that was required to formulate guidelines on inspection and recommend consequent actions. Such a task is always difficult, as a balance has to be struck between what is practical and achievable, and what a litigious society might consider safe and proper: the 'precautionary principle' binds us all. It would be all too easy to impose strict guidelines that could close plant at high, and unacceptable, cost.

The essence of a deaerator is a pressure vessel some 3–5 m in diameter, operating at between 100 and 200 °C and up to 1.25 MPa pressure. With a wall thickness of about 25 mm, such a cylinder can be considered as thin-walled. In any pressurized cylinder, the hoop stresses are greater than the longitudinal stresses and so the most dangerous direction for a flaw is in an axial (longitudinal) direction, because these dominant hoop stresses will open such a crack.

EXERCISE 5.7

Would you recommend that surface-breaking flaws or embedded flaws are the ones to be most concerned about?

Hint: you might want to look at the Y calibrations for edge-cracked and centre-cracked geometries.

According to Exercise 5.7, surface flaws are worse than embedded flaws. This is just as well, because surface-breaking cracks are much easier to find than embedded cracks. The workhorse of surface-breaking crack detection is magnetic particle inspection (MPI) – you can do it anywhere (Figure 5.44a), which suits our problem, and it is very good at showing up fine cracks (Figure 5.44b). What it doesn't tell you, however, is the depth of the crack that is found.

7.1 Applying fracture mechanics

For a thin-walled cylinder, taking into account the radius of the cylinder does not make a huge difference to the values of *Y*; so, for this assessment I shall ignore the radius of the pipe for the purpose of calculating *K* and also assume that all flaws are on the inside surface. In practice, all the cracks originated on the inner surfaces of the deaerators, and experience suggests that cracking is generally limited to areas of a vessel that have not been post-weld heat-treated.

Because MPI can produce only a crack *length* and says nothing about the depth, or shape, of a crack, the first task for the Working Group was to get some data by examining existing deaerators during outages (jargon for when the plant is

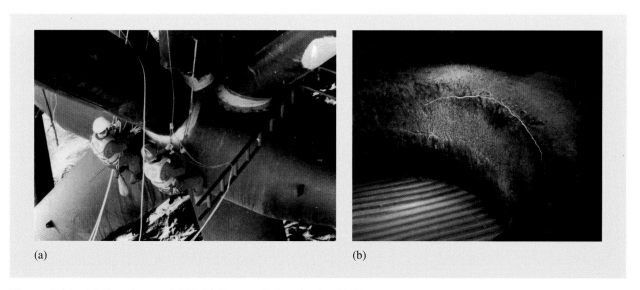

(a)   (b)

Figure 5.44   (a) Carrying out MPI; (b) fine crack found using MPI

not running). A sample from a cracked weldment in a highly stressed weld from the deaerator at Ferrybridge power station was examined in detail using standard metallographic sections. It was found that cracks were surface-breaking and irregular, and there was some branching.

It is not possible to model such complicated shapes, but cracks growing by fatigue from the surface can usefully be modelled as being elliptical in shape. Figure 5.45 shows the dimensioning: the mean radius is r, the wall thickness is t, the length of the surface indication is $2c$ and the depth (length) of the crack is a.

The K calibration factor, Y, will vary with the crack penetration, a/t, and the aspect ratio of the ellipse, a/c. Also, Y will vary around the crack border, but not by a significant amount in the context of this problem.

K around the border of a semi-elliptical crack will be a maximum at the crack's deepest point. So, how will a semi-elliptical crack change shape under fatigue loading?

The only theory I have is the Paris law, which states that the rate of change of crack length varies like ΔK. This suggests that, as K (and therefore ΔK) is a maximum at the deepest point of the crack, under a cyclic loading the deepest point will grow faster than the edges and so the crack will tunnel into the wall.

Fortunately this is not the case and cracks do not tunnel into the wall of a pressure vessel. As the surface is less constrained than the centre, the plastic zone is larger; thus the micro-mechanisms of the fatigue process cause faster growth at the edges and the crack broadens out (i.e. becomes more elliptical) as it grows. The Paris equation does not model this process.

Because the crack gets longer more rapidly than it gets deeper, it becomes more obvious to the NDE inspector with a technique that finds only surface-breaking flaws; just as well, really!

You should recall from Part 1 that NDE stands for non-destructive evaluation.

EXERCISE 5.8

As $2c$ gets very long, what value of Y would you expect for a crack with a small value of a?

Hint: have a look at Figure 5.45b.

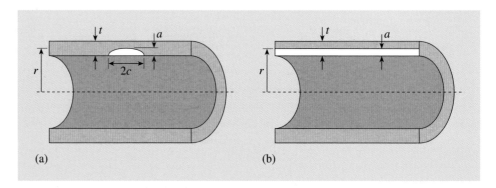

(a)   (b)

Figure 5.45   (a) Elliptical and (b) long crack in a pipe

EXERCISE 5.9

Are longer (in the surface-breaking dimension) semi-elliptical cracks more or less severe than shorter cracks of the same depth? Experiment with the K calculator, starting with a semi-circular crack in a vessel with a 25 mm wall thickness.

The Working Group then chose a representative example of the loading conditions of a deaerator. Nearly all the vessels are designed to the US ASME Code, resulting in vessel wall thicknesses up to, but generally less than, 25 mm, made from ubiquitous carbon steel grades.

ASME was founded in 1880 as the American Society of Mechanical Engineers.

The typical geometry and loading that the Working Group chose are as follows:

Geometry

Mean diameter: 4 m

Wall thickness: 25 mm

Loading

Normal operating pressure: 1.5 MPa

Maximum operating pressure: 2 MPa

Table 5.2 gives the material properties specification for the representative vessel.

Table 5.2   Material properties specification for typical deaerator

Temperature/°C	σ_{yield}/MPa	σ_{UTS}/MPa	Weld K_{IC}/ MPa √m	Plate K_{IC}/ MPa √m	Weld $K_{0.2}$/ MPa √m	Plate $K_{0.2}$/ MPa √m
100	200	400	120	110	unknown	160
200	200	400	140	130	unknown	160

SAQ 5.8 (Part 1 revision)

Why did the Working Group choose the maximum value of wall thickness for their representative vessel?

SAQ 5.9 (Block 1 revision)

What is the membrane hoop stress in the wall of the representative vessel at the maximum operating pressure?

The next step in our consideration of this problem is to estimate a critical crack length for brittle fracture. We do not know the shape of the crack, so we can try a couple of sample shapes, assuming that they are surface-breaking and on the inside surface.

SAQ 5.10 (Part 1 revision)

What is the critical crack size for a long surface crack? Model this using the through-thickness edge-crack geometry in the K calculator. (Remember that when calculating critical crack length in the K calculator, you need to hit the 'Calculate' button after entering the values.)

Is the answer highly dependent on whether the higher or the lower value of toughness is used?

EXERCISE 5.10

What is the critical crack size for a semicircular crack?

Note: you cannot use the 'Critical crack length' option in the calculator to calculate this directly, because it calculates a for a fixed value of 2c. So you'll have to perform the calculation indirectly, using the 'K$_{IC}$' option. If you input increasing values of a whilst keeping a/c equal to 1 by varying 2c, then when the calculated K$_{IC}$ equals 110 MPa √m you'll have the critical size of a semicircular crack.

This takes us only a little further, but let's review what you've discovered. If the crack is an edge crack then the surface indication of the edge crack is notionally infinite, so finding the crack will not be a problem, and the section is more than halfway cracked through when LEFM predicts brittle fracture.

If the crack is semicircular, then it can fully penetrate the vessel wall without causing brittle failure. (Although the semicircular crack grows all the way through without breaking, we cannot automatically assume that the vessel will leak if this happens, as corrosion products tend to fill cracks and the vessel is lagged, so seeping of water might not be seen.) However, the geometry of the semicircular crack changes once the crack has penetrated the wall. Ignoring the curved ends of the crack and the radius of curvature of the pipe, we can model this as a through-thickness, central crack in an infinite plate under tension (Figure 5.46).

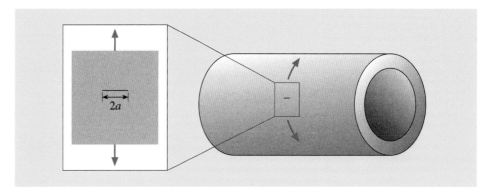

Figure 5.46   The centre-crack diagram superimposed on a crack in a pipe

EXERCISE 5.11

If the semicircular crack can be modelled to grow as a centre-cracked plate in tension (ignoring the pipe radius) once it has penetrated the wall, how long does it need to grow before LEFM predicts failure?

Note: the K calculator is for a finite-width geometry; so, to model a long pipe, either do the sum by hand with the Y calibration for an infinite plate (Y = 1) or put a very large value of 2W into the calculator.

The result of Exercise 5.11 shows that even if the crack grows all the way through the wall, it has to grow to a significant length before it causes failure in a brittle manner.

If any of these calculations had predicted brittle failure from anything other than long, deep cracks we could have continued with LEFM theory. However, brittle failure of this tough steel was always unlikely, so to pursue the case further we will need to use an FAD.

7.2 Applying the failure assessment diagram

Given that brittle failure of the pipe is unlikely, the next step is to assess whether plastic collapse could occur. For this, you will switch to using the R6 calculator.

EXERCISE 5.12

(a) Using the lower value of toughness, use the calculator to generate the assessment point for a long edge crack, 14 mm deep, on the R6 FAD for this pipe geometry. What type of failure would you expect?

(b) At what length of edge crack does the R6 calculator predict failure? (You'll have to change the crack length manually until the assessment point is close to the curve and the reserve factor is close to 1.)

I am considering a tough material at a high temperature, so I might sensibly use the $K_{0.2}$ value of material toughness, 160 MPa $\sqrt{m}$ (Table 5.2); but if you try this you'll find that it doesn't make much difference. I calculate that it increases the critical crack length to about 8.6 mm.

So, a very long (and thus easily detectable) crack can grow about a third of the way through the thickness before failure, which suggests that the ordinary design loading is good. So this brings us back to our starting point for this design analysis: why are these vessels blowing up?

SAQ 5.11 (Learning outcome 5.6)

Suggest another source of stress that might be leading to failure, in addition to the design stresses.

As the answer to SAQ 5.11 suggested, looking at the effects of residual stress would be sensible. However, because the effects of residual stress tend to be more localized than the applied loading, we must deal with more realistic crack shapes than the long cracks used so far.

So, you will now use the R6 calculator geometry for a semi-elliptical crack and include the presence of secondary residual stresses due to welding.

SAQ 5.12 (Learning outcomes 5.4 and 5.5)

Use the R6 calculator to find the reserve factors on load, under the design stresses, for internal semicircular cracks with surface-breaking indications (the length $2c$) of 10 mm, 25 mm and 40 mm. (Remember that if the crack is semicircular then a is half of $2c$.) Use the lower value of material toughness.

You should have found in SAQ 5.12 that all the assessment points were in the EPFM to plastic collapse region in the diagram. So it might be more appropriate to use the $K_{0.2}$ value of toughness, which anticipates some plasticity, rather than K_{IC}. If we repeat the calculations using $K_{0.2}$, we obtain the values given in Table 5.3. An example calculation is shown in Figure 5.47.

Table 5.3   Calculating reserve factors on load using $K_{0.2}$

a/mm	K_r	L_r	Reserve
5	0.08	0.80	1.89
12.5	0.14	0.80	1.68
20	0.19	0.81	1.52

Let's now investigate the effect of the residual stress.

SAQ 5.13 (Learning outcomes 5.5 and 5.6)

Using the $K_{0.2}$ value of toughness, repeat SAQ 5.12, this time assuming that there are residual welding stresses equivalent to yield. Remember that the residual stresses are entered into the R6 calculator in the box labelled 'Secondary stress'. You should carry out the calculations twice:

(a) assuming that the residual stresses act in the parent plate

(b) assuming that the crack is in the weld metal. As we don't have a value of $K_{0.2}$ for the weld metal (bits of weld metal tend not to be of the dimensions needed for fracture toughness samples), use the K_{IC} value (which is 120 MPa √m).

It can be seen from the answer to SAQ 5.13 that once the residual stresses are included, the crack with the 40 mm surface indication approaches failure.

When the margin becomes this small, we stop using simplifying assumptions and see if refining our model of the crack geometry makes things worse or better. So I will now look at a crack that is shallower than the semicircular crack I assumed, because it has been found in practice that this is the way that cracks tend to grow.

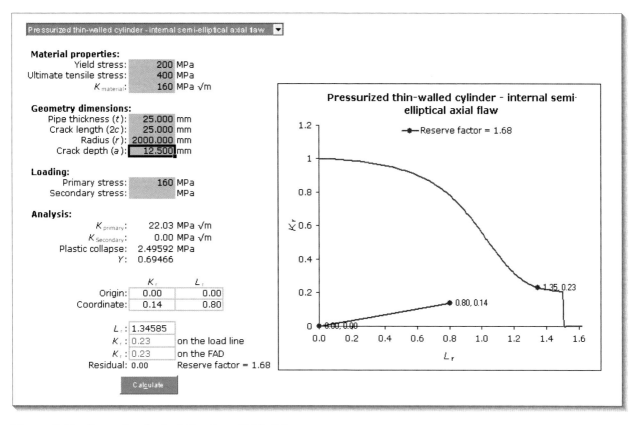

Figure 5.47   Example of calculation from Table 5.3

SAQ 5.14 (Learning outcome 5.5)

Repeat SAQ 5.13(b) with the same length of surface indication, but assuming that the crack is only half as deep as a semicircular crack. Use the results that you get from the R6 calculator to complete Table 5.4.

Table 5.4   Reserve values to be filled in for a halved

$2c$/mm	a/mm	Reserve
10	2.5	
25	6.25	
40	10	

SAQ 5.15 (Learning outcomes 5.4 and 5.5)

Assume that a crack in the weld metal that has a 40 mm long surface indication has actually grown all the way through the wall. Again assuming that the residual welding stresses are equal to yield, what would be the reserve factor on load? Make sure you use the appropriate geometry in the R6 calculator for this problem.

The 40 mm long surface indication is pushing the boundary on all the assumptions made so far. There is some reserve on the 25 mm long surface indication, but not a huge amount. The modelling of the problem that you have just carried out should convince you that there is cause for concern with the design as it stands.

To pursue the line of argument further you would have to know more about inspection experience and practice.

Here is what the Working Group recommended.

> In order to ensure that deaerator inspections are carried out to a common standard the Deaerator Inspection Working Group issues the following guidance:
>
> Inspections are to be carried out by MPI from the inside surface of the deaerator storage vessel. Where defect indications are reported it is necessary to decide whether to:
>
>> leave the defect
>>
>> grind out the defect
>>
>> grind out and repair-weld the defect.
>
> The decision on what action to take will depend on whether the defect is crack-like, whether it is an initial construction defect, whether it has initiated in service, its size and location, the stress level in the vessel and the past and future operation of the unit. The decision should be made by the appropriate regional specialist.
>
> The MPI inspection may reveal a large number of defect indications, many of which may be too small to be of any concern with regard to vessel integrity. In order to reduce the number of defect indications on which the regional specialist has to make decisions a minimum reporting length of 15 mm has been set. It is assumed that any defect of less than 15 mm in length does not put the integrity of the vessel at risk and will not grow to a length at which failure would occur during the life of the vessel. The reportable defect length of 15 mm is qualified by the need to recognize that adjacent defects may interact.
>
> In addition to the minimum defect reporting length the Group are recommending a defect length below which no further action need be taken by the regional specialist. I.e. any defect of less than this length is immediately acceptable in any deaerator and can be left in the vessel. This length is set at 20 mm. This difference between minimum reporting length and acceptable defect length is deliberate and designed to ensure that decisions on defect acceptance are made by specialists, rather than NDT operators.
>
> Defects outside these criteria are not necessarily unacceptable, it is simply that they need further consideration.

What you should know from this section:

- How to approach a practical problem using an FAD.

- How to use the R6 calculator, in conjunction with the K calculator, to analyse failure for different materials and geometries.

8 SUMMARY

You have been guided through a set of speculative numerical experiments that followed the same reasoning as that of very experienced engineers on a national panel where the stakes were of some significance – lives were being lost.

This was a somewhat unusual process, in terms of both engineering and educational practices, because there was not a specific design case or a particular failure. Rather, there was a series of assumptions that created a picture of a generic problem. None of our values were absolutes and there were no correct numerical answers on the way to a conclusion.

The R6 FAD is unusual compared with most techniques presented in engineering courses because it contains both practical and theoretical understandings in a set of procedures that reflect best practice.

Using the theory and the tools presented in this course, we have come to the same conclusions as the Working Group about the potential severity of different types and sizes of cracks, which is a remarkable achievement.

I hope that you have gained some understanding of good engineering ways to think about problems, as well as the ability to drive an FAD.

This brings us almost to the end of the course. In the final part, we will look at some case studies that integrate aspects of what you have already studied, and indicate additional factors that can lead to fracture of which you should be aware.

LEARNING OUTCOMES

After studying Block 2 Part 5 you should be able to do the following.

5.1 Outline the different measures of fracture toughness that exist and how they are obtained practically.

5.2 Calculate a material's flow stress as the mean of its yield strength and UTS.

5.3 Calculate the plastic collapse load for a component, and compare it with the expected in-service load.

5.4 Estimate the reserve factor on load using an FAD.

5.5 Use the R6 calculator to perform safety assessments, given appropriate input data.

5.6 Understand and use residual stresses when using the R6 calculator.

ANSWERS TO EXERCISES

EXERCISE 5.1

Applying the fracture mechanics equation predicts a stress of just over 425 MPa and, hence, a failure load of 425 MPa × 0.03 m × 0.03 m, which is about 383 kN.

EXERCISE 5.2

The flow stress is the mean of the yield stress and the UTS, so we have:

(a) σ_{flow} = (280 MPa + 520 MPa)/2 = 400 MPa

(b) σ_{flow} = (420 MPa + 550 MPa)/2 = 485 MPa

EXERCISE 5.3

Clearly not using the sample shown in Figure 5.10! But in principle, yes. However, to produce a valid brittle fracture toughness measure for a material this tough you would probably need a test piece the size of a filing cabinet or two, and there wouldn't be a machine big enough to break it.

EXERCISE 5.4

The intersection with the curve is in the EPFM tearing region of the FAD, but over towards the plastic collapse region.

EXERCISE 5.5

I can simply increase the crack length by increments and show the assessment points on the diagram to get a picture of how quickly the points approach the boundary, where failure is indicated. I shall plot points at 0.5 mm increments (Figure 5.48).

This soon produces failure, at about 3 mm.

EXERCISE 5.6

It will move the cut-off line to the left, because the 'gap' between yield stress and ultimate stress will be smaller, so the flow stress will be a smaller multiple of the yield stress.

EXERCISE 5.7

From the argument for an edge crack having a higher *Y* than half of a centre-cracked panel – surface-breaking flaws allow the mouth of the crack to gape, thus feeding more *K* into the crack tip – you would expect the surface-breaking flaw to be the most severe. Also, an inside, surface-breaking crack tends to be worse because internal pressure can also act to open the crack surfaces.

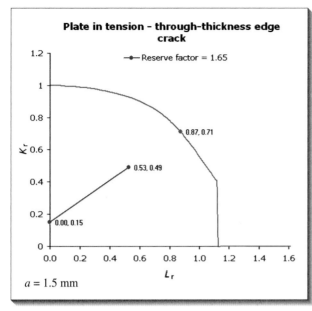

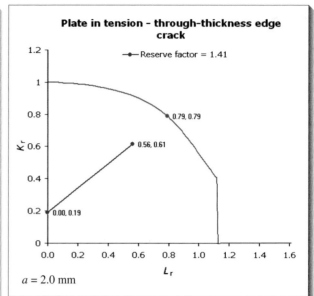

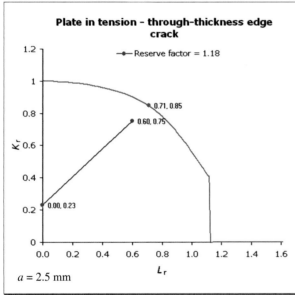

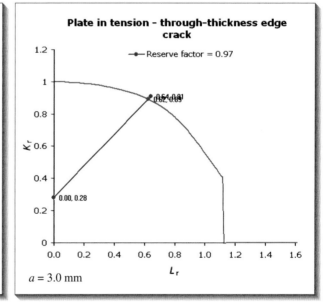

Figure 5.48 Plotting points at 0.5 mm increments

EXERCISE 5.8

As $2c$ becomes very large compared with a, the crack geometry approaches that of a single edge-cracked plate (Figure 5.45b). The Y calibration for a very long, single edge crack starts at 1.12 and increases rapidly as the crack penetrates the depth. So, if the crack is shallow, Y should be 1.12.

If you experiment with the K calculator for the semi-elliptical geometry you will find that this is approximately correct.

EXERCISE 5.9

A semicircular crack that is 10% of the way through the wall (a = 2.5 mm and $2c$ = 5 mm) shows a Y of 0.66 (Figure 5.49a). Double the surface length ($2c$ = 10 mm), keeping the depth constant, and Y increases to 0.9 (Figure 5.49b). So, longer cracks are more severe. However, longer cracks are also easier to find by MPI than short cracks.

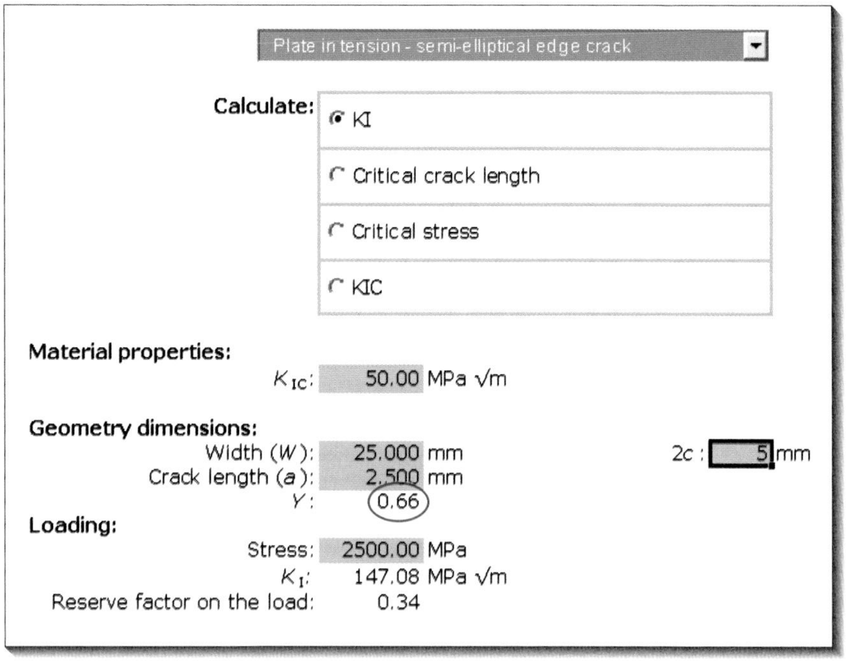

(a)

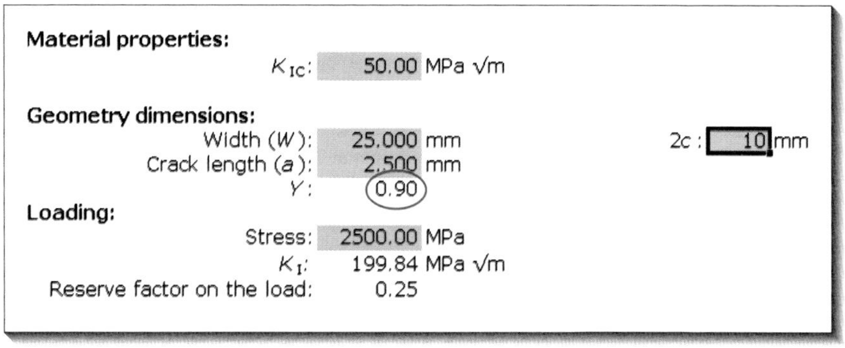

(b)

Figure 5.49 Y values for (a) $2c$ = 5 mm and (b) $2c$ = 10 mm, keeping a constant

EXERCISE 5.10

Doing this I find that I can 'grow' the crack all the way through the wall without reaching the critical value of 110 MPa √m (my maximum value of K_{IC} is 35.47 MPa √m). So the crack will never cause brittle fracture in this geometry.

EXERCISE 5.11

Using a K_{IC} of 110 MPa √m, I put an arbitrary 5 m into the calculator for $2W$, to represent a long pipe. The calculator slowly chuntered up to a critical crack length, $2a$, of about 300 mm and showed a Y of 1, which was comforting (Figure 5.50).

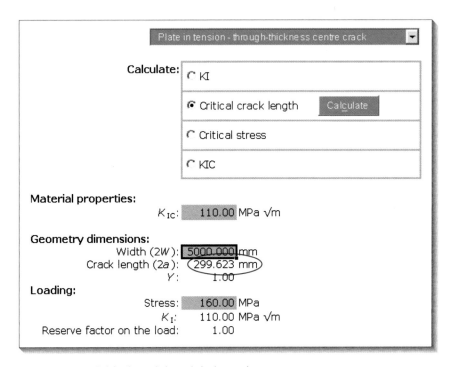

Figure 5.50   Critical crack length in long pipe

EXERCISE 5.12

(a) Using the lowest K_{IC} of 110 MPa √m and a 14 mm deep edge crack, I found a reserve factor of 0.54, so the FAD predicts failure by a mechanism that involves tearing or plastic collapse (Figure 5.51).

(b) Trying some lower values of crack length predicts a crack length at failure of around 7.5 mm (Figure 5.52).

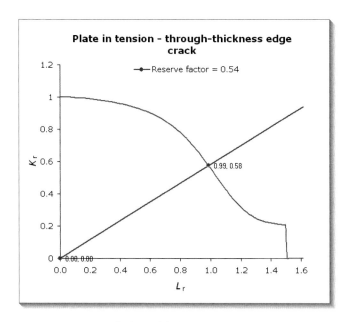

Figure 5.51   Prediction of failure by tearing or plastic collapse

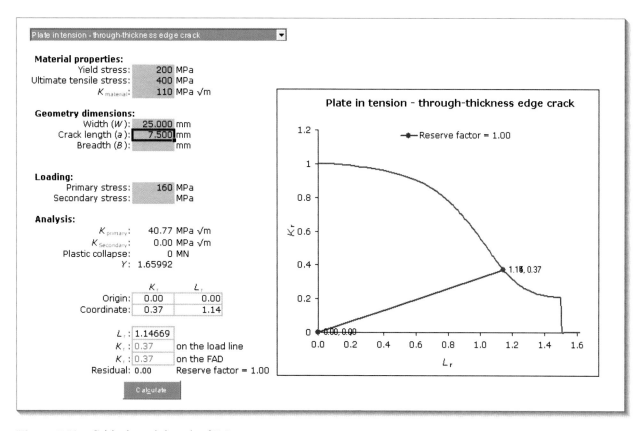

Figure 5.52   Critical crack length of 7.5 mm

ANSWERS TO SELF-ASSESSMENT QUESTIONS

SAQ 5.1

We have K_{IC} for brittle failure and $K_{0.2}$ for ductile tearing. There are also CTOD methods available.

SAQ 5.2

The flow stress is the average of yield stress and UTS, which is 450 MPa. The ratio of the flow to yield stresses is 450 MPa/400 MPa, which is 1.125. This produces the specific diagram for this material shown in Figure 5.53.

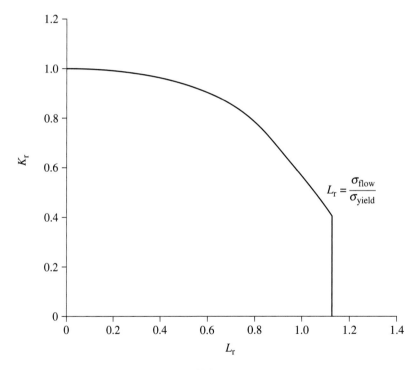

Figure 5.53   Adding the R6 cut-off line

SAQ 5.3

The Y calibration factor for this geometry is in your K calculator; alternatively, it can be read off Figure 5.1 or calculated using:

$$Y = 1.12 - 0.231\frac{a}{W} + 10.55\left(\frac{a}{W}\right)^2 - 21.72\left(\frac{a}{W}\right)^3 + 30.39\left(\frac{a}{W}\right)^4$$

It doesn't matter what you use, but looking at the equation, for an a/W of 0.1, Y to a first approximation is about 1.2.

The stress due to the design pressure of 15 MPa, using $\sigma = pr/t$, is (15 MPa × 0.12 m)/0.01 m, which is 180 MPa, a respectable 45% of yield.

Using the equation $K = Y\sigma\sqrt{\pi a}$, I have:

$$K = 1.2 \times 180 \text{ MPa} \times \sqrt{\pi \times 0.001 \text{ m}}$$
$$\approx 12 \text{ MPa} \sqrt{m}$$

K_r is the ratio of K to $K_{material}$, so I need to calculate K_{IC} from the C_v of 15 J.

The SINTAP recommendation of $K_{IC} = 12C_v^{0.5}$ suggests a lower-bound fracture toughness of 46 MPa √m. So:

$$K_r \approx 12 \text{ MPa } \sqrt{m}/46 \text{ MPa } \sqrt{m} \approx 0.26$$

SAQ 5.4

Using the equation $\sigma_{yield} = (p_L \times r)/t$:

$$p_L = (\sigma_{yield} \times t)/r = (400 \text{ MPa} \times 0.009 \text{ m})/0.12 \text{ m} = 30 \text{ MPa}$$

So:

$$L_r = p/p_L = 15 \text{ MPa}/30 \text{ MPa} = 0.5$$

SAQ 5.5

I measure this as about 2.

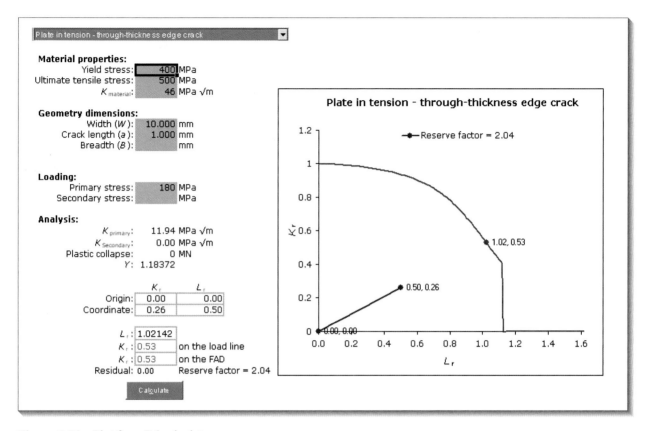

Figure 5.54   Plot from R6 calculator

SAQ 5.6

The plot from the R6 calculator is shown in Figure 5.54.

SAQ 5.7

I used the R6 calculator. Figure 5.55 shows FADs for the pipe with a residual welding stress of (a) 20% of yield, (b) 80% of yield and (c) 100% of yield.

SAQ 5.8

Because a bigger section is more likely to produce brittle fractures.

SAQ 5.9

We are interested only in the stress at the maximum operating pressure. The hoop stress is given by:

$$\sigma = pr/t = (2 \text{ MPa} \times 2 \text{ m})/0.025 \text{ m} = 160 \text{ MPa}$$

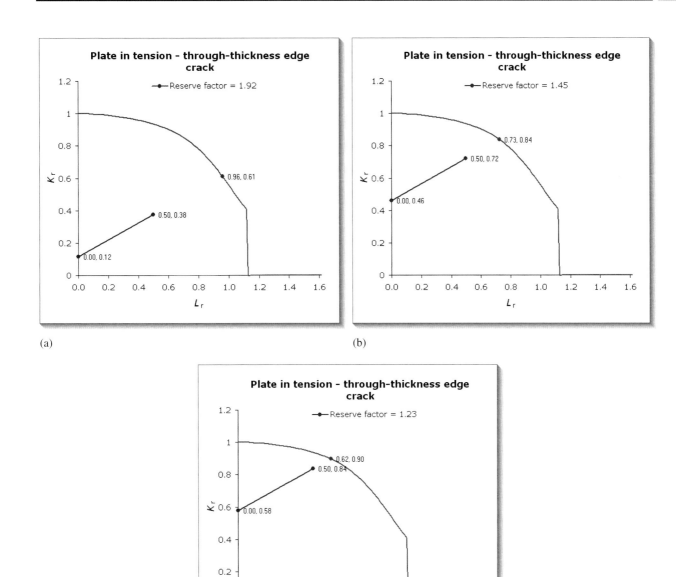

(a)

(b)

(c)

Figure 5.55   FAD for pipe with residual welding stress of (a) 20%, (b) 80% and (c) 100% of yield

SAQ 5.10

Using the edge-crack geometry with the lowest K_{IC} of 110 MPa $\sqrt{m}$ in the plate, the K calculator says that for an edge crack the critical crack length is 13.7 mm through the 25 mm wall (Figure 5.56).

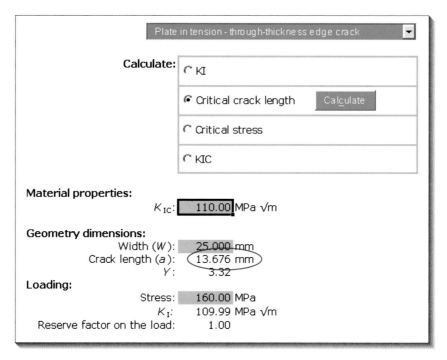

Figure 5.56   Critical crack length for minimum toughness value

For brittle fracture the maximum value of toughness is 140 MPa $\sqrt{m}$, which returns a critical crack length of about 15 mm, so there is not an enormous dependence on the toughness.

SAQ 5.11

Perhaps there are loads on the vessel that haven't been considered. However, we certainly haven't thought about the residual stresses at welds in the vessel; we should look at those next.

SAQ 5.12

If the cracks are semicircular then the values of a are half those of $2c$: 5 mm, 12.5 mm and 20 mm respectively.

Using the R6 calculator with a K_{IC} of 110 MPa $\sqrt{m}$, I get the results given in Table 5.5. An example calculation is shown in Figure 5.57.

Table 5.5   Calculating reserve factors on load

a/mm	K_r	L_r	Reserve
5	0.12	0.80	1.77
12.5	0.20	0.80	1.52
20	0.27	0.81	1.40

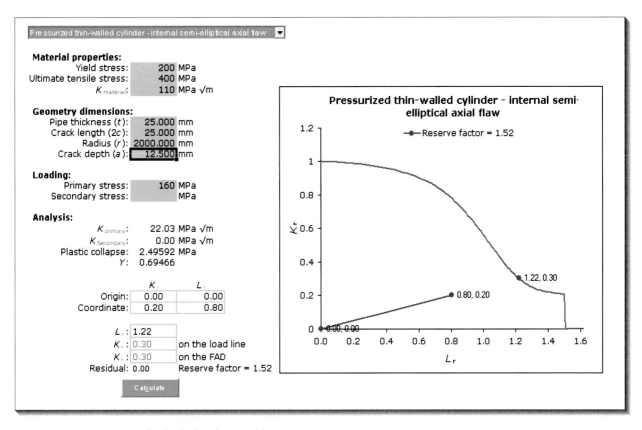

Figure 5.57   Example of calculation from Table 5.5

SAQ 5.13

In both cases the yield stress is 200 MPa.

(a) With residual stress assumed to act in the plate, the results of the calculations are given in Table 5.6. An example calculation is shown in Figure 5.58.

Table 5.6   Reserve factors with residual stresses acting in the parent plate

a/mm	Reserve
5	1.64
12.5	1.43
20	1.31

(b) Table 5.7 gives the results of the calculations when the crack is assumed to be in the weld metal. An example calculation is shown in Figure 5.59.

Table 5.7   Reserve factors with the crack in the weld metal

a/mm	Reserve
5	1.51
12.5	1.33
20	1.18

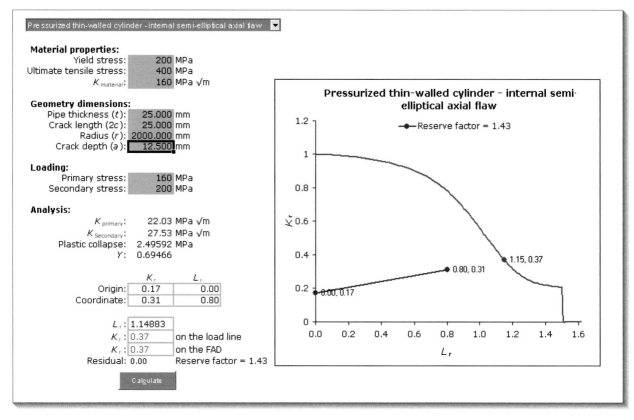

Figure 5.58   Example of calculation from Table 5.6

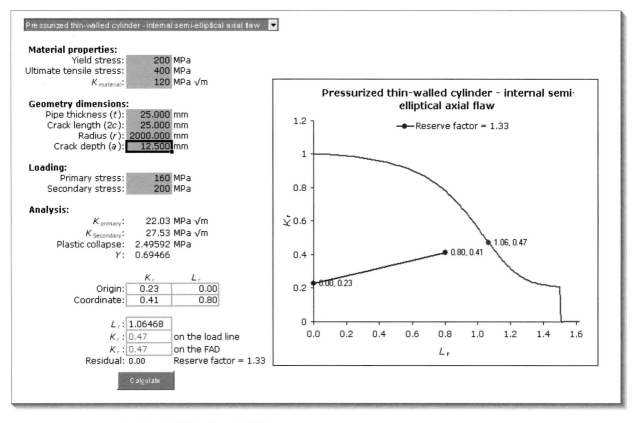

Figure 5.59   Example of calculation from Table 5.7

SAQ 5.14

Yield is 200 MPa and K_{IC} is 120 MPa √m, so the results are given in Table 5.8. An example calculation is shown in Figure 5.60.

Table 5.8   Reserve values for *a* halved

2*c*/mm	*a*/mm	Reserve
10	2.5	1.53
25	6.25	1.35
40	10	1.23

This gives us a little more leeway on the 40 mm surface indication, but not much.

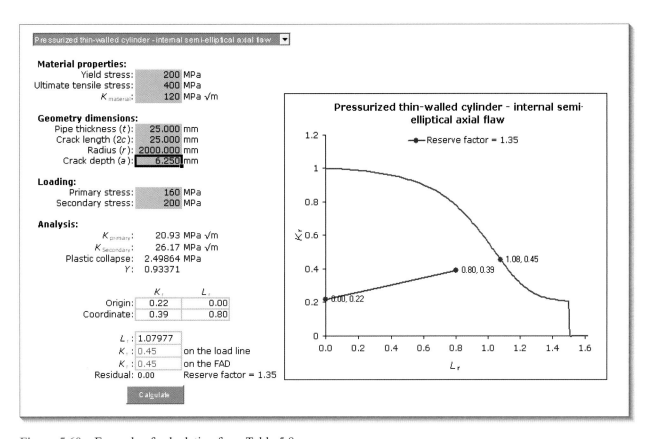

Figure 5.60   Example of calculation from Table 5.8

SAQ 5.15

Switching to the appropriate geometry, the through-wall semi-circular flaw, the R6 curve predicts a reserve of 1.02 (Figure 5.61).

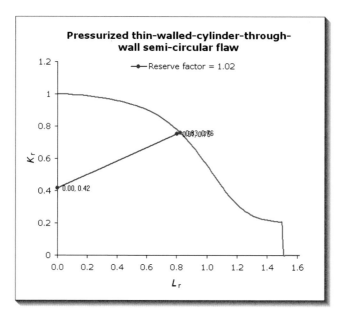

Figure 5.61   Reserve of 1.02 predicted using the correct geometry

REFERENCES

CEGB Deaerator Inspection Working Party (1986) *Immediately Acceptable Defect Lengths in Deaerator Storage Vessels*, Central Electricity Generating Board.

Strauss, S.D. (1983) 'Concern rises for safety of feedwater deaerators', *POWER*.

ACKNOWLEDGEMENTS

Grateful acknowledgement is made to the following sources:

FIGURES

Figure 5.7: Materials Testing Institute, University of Stuttgart.

Figure 5.8: Courtesy of S. Slatcher.

Figure 5.9: © John Hancock, Glasgow University.

Figure 5.15: Courtesy of M R Goldthorpe and Associates.

Figure 5.19: From Mathers, G. (2005) CTOD Testing, at www.twi.co.uk. © TWI Ltd.

Figure 5.31: Courtesy of Taylor Forge Engineered Systems.

Figures 5.40 and 5.41: Courtesy of TWI Ltd.

Figure 5.43: Strauss, S.D.(1983) 'Concern rises for safety of feedwater deaerators', *POWER* magazine, TradeFair Group Publications.

Figure 5.44(a): Courtesy of CAN Group.

Figure 5.44(b): © 2001 Iowa State University. All rights reserved.

Every effort has been made to contact copyright holders. If any have been inadvertently overlooked the publishers will be pleased to make the necessary arrangements at the first opportunity.

COURSE TEAM ACKNOWLEDGEMENTS

This part was prepared for the course team by Adrian Demaid.

T357 COURSE TEAM

Dr Michael Fitzpatrick (course team chair)

Andy Harding (course manager)

Jackie Burnicle (course manager)

ACADEMIC STAFF

Dr Alun Armstrong

Professor Adrian Demaid

Professor Chris Earl

Professor Lyndon Edwards

Dr Salih Gungor

Michael Hush

Dr Peter Lewis

Dr Jim Moffatt

Dr Ed Murphy

Dr Martin Rist

EXTERNAL ASSESSOR

Professor Lindsay Greer, University of Cambridge

SUPPORT STAFF

Debbie Derbyshire (course team secretary)

Colin Gagg

Stan Hiller

Gordon Imlach

Pete Ledgard

Sheila Taylor

PRODUCTION TEAM

Kirsten Barnett

Annette Booz

Philippa Broadbent

Lisa Carrick

Teresa Cox

Sarah Crompton

Daphne Cross

Anna Edgley-Smith

Vicky Eves

Chris French

Carol Houghton

Jonathan Martyn

Margaret McManus

Katie Meade

Lara Mynors

Deana Plummer

Lynn Short

Susanne Umerski